Natural Healing for Cats

Susanne Bönisch

Sterling Publishing Co., Inc.
New York

Contents

The author's many years of experience are the basis for the treatment methods and tips suggested in this book. However, since every illness is different, neither the author nor the publishers have any control over how the reader chooses to utilize the information in this book, and they are not responsible for consequences that result from its use. This information is not a substitute for responsible, proper veterinary care.

Photos: Monika Wegler, Munich
Illustrations: Bettina Buresch, Munich
Translated by Elisabeth Reinersmann

Library of Congress Cataloging-in-Publication Data

Bönisch, Susan.
　　[Katzen natürlich heilen. English]
　　Natural healing for cats / by Susan Bonisch.
　　　　p.　cm.
　　Includes index.
　　ISBN 0-8069-8122-9
　　1. Cats—Diseases—Alternative treatment.　2. Holistic veterinary medicine.　3. Cats—Health.　I. Title.
SF985.B6613　1966
636.8'08955—dc20
　　　　　　　　　　　　　　　　　　　　96-26157
　　　　　　　　　　　　　　　　　　　　　　CIP

10　9　8　7　6　5　4　3　2　1

Published 1996 by Sterling Publishing Company, Inc.
387 Park Avenue South, New York, N.Y. 10016
Originally published by Mosaic Verlag GmbH, Munich
under the title Katzen Natürlich Heilen
© 1994 by Mosaic Verlag
English translation © 1996 by Sterling Publishing Co., Inc.
Distributed in Canada by Sterling Publishing
% Canadian Manda Group, One Atlantic Avenue, Suite 105
Toronto, Ontario, Canada M6K 3E7
Distributed in Great Britain and Europe by Cassell PLC
Wellington House, 125 Strand, London WC2R 0BB, England
Distributed in Australia by Capricorn Link (Australia) Pty Ltd.
P.O. Box 6651, Baulkham Hills, Business Centre, NSW 2153, Australia
Manufactured in the United States of America
Printed in Hong Kong
All rights reserved

Sterling ISBN 0-8069-8122-9

Contents

A windowsill is a favorite spot, particularly for indoor cats.

In this book I want to give cat lovers information and tips on how to use natural healing methods to care for their sick pets. I'm not suggesting the use of natural methods as substitutes or alternatives to conventional medicine; rather, I want cat lovers to use them as adjuncts to or extensions of conventional medicine. In general, a responsible nonmedical practitioner always works with a veterinarian, who will examine and treat any illnesses that are beyond the capabilities of the practitioner. Sometimes, natural healing methods are a bit more time-consuming than the methods of allopathic (the use of drugs to alleviate symptoms) medicine, requiring more patience and commitment from the cat owner. The case histories from my practice make it clear that patience and commitment are worthwhile.

I always pay special attention to the affected organs or the injured part of the body when I design a therapy, but, as a nonmedical practitioner, I also take into consideration each cat's particular situation and environment. This may place extra demands on the owner, but one of the most important prerequisites for a healthy animal is an owner who is sensitive to its needs, including proper nutrition and proper handling.

Healthy cats react spontaneously to any external stimulus, regardless of whether it is the movement of prey or simply a toy.

The Most Important Natural Healing Methods

TIP

Many people believe that treatments using natural healing methods are tedious and time-consuming; this may or may not be the case. In many instances, these treatments achieve results in a surprisingly short amount of time.

Natural Healing— What Is It?

Natural healing techniques teach us how to address health problems and injuries with natural methods. That holds true for animals as well as people. Utilizing natural remedies means that we don't use chemical or pharmaceutical preparations; every remedy comes exclusively and directly from nature.

The different natural treatments known today are a combination of autonomous methods that should never be in conflict or competition with allopathic (the use of drugs to alleviate symptoms) medicine. Sometimes, the best interests of the patients may require using a combination of natural methods and conventional medicine.

Under no circumstances should you use natural methods hastily or indiscriminately. An accurate diagnosis is essential. For that reason, responsible practitioners use modern diagnostic methods, such as lab analysis of blood, stool, and urine, as well as X rays.

A natural practitioner will always try to treat the whole animal, including the

medicine for people, as well as for animals. The therapy consists of exposing diseased or injured parts of the body to an artificially created magnetic field for a few minutes. Scientists don't know yet how magnetic field therapy actually works. However, using a specific photo technique, researchers have noticed that when they expose an affected area to a small electrical energy flow, the temperature and flow of blood in that area increases, which in turn increases the oxygen available in the tissue.

We usually use magnetic field therapy for chronic inflammation, as well as for all degenerative bone and joint problems related to age or injuries.

The magnetic field surrounding Earth is a natural phenomenon. Electrical energy, or more precisely, the movement or flow of electrical energy can create a magnetic field artificially. The strength or magnitude of such a magnetic field depends on, among other things, the prevailing electrical current. For different illnesses, the practitioner will treat the patient in a field of relatively higher or lower magnetic strength.

psychological state and not just the symptoms. When you bring an injured cat into the office, a practitioner will be just as concerned about the psychological shock the animal might have suffered as he or she will be about the injury and the physical condition.

But used exclusively, natural healing methods do have their limitations; for example, when the patient has lost its capacity for self-healing, when essential life-sustaining functions (such as insulin production) have stopped, or when optimum healing can only occur with surgery. In such cases, the patient should see a veterinarian.

Magnetic Field Therapy

Magnetic field therapy is a proven healing method often used in conventional

Leeches

The medicinal leech (*Hirudo medivinalis*), up to 6in (15cm) long, has a sucking organ on both ends. It attaches itself to the animal, bites through the skin, and sucks blood. Depending on its size, a leech can suck ½ teaspoon to 4 teaspoons (2 to 20 ml) of blood, which it stores in its expandable stomach.

Natural practitioners use leeches raised specifically for medicinal purposes. The practitioner places them on the patient. When they have had their fill, they fall off by themselves. Afterwards, the area may bleed slightly for several hours, but you don't need to cover it.

The therapeutic effect is at least partially due to the decrease in the volume of blood in that specific area; the leeches' meal is a kind of bloodletting. In addition, the leeches' saliva, transferred to

the patient's skin, contains substances that act as a local anesthetic and increase the circulation and coagulation of the blood. The application of leeches can often bring astounding results. For instance, when the patient suffers from arthritis and circulation problems, the improvement usually begins within twelve hours after the treatment.

Homeopathy

Many people think that homeopathy, one of the best-known forms of alternative healing, is the same as natural healing. However, homeopathy is only one of the methods used, even if it is one of the most prominent.

Begun at the end of the eighteenth century by Dr. Samual Hahnemann (1755–1843), homeopathy means "heal-ing with like." The basic principle states that whatever is making an organism sick can also heal it. According to the "law of similarity," you treat a patient with a medication containing an extremely diluted dose of a substance that, given in high doses, would cause an illness similar to what the patient has. On first thought, this seems rather paradoxical, but it works. Adherents believe that homeopathic medications activate an organism's own capacity for healing and that medications need to be geared very specifically to the symptoms of an illness.

In this context, it is interesting to note that in homeopathy, the term for this process is not "diluting the substances," but "increasing their potency." During the production process, you don't simply dilute the medication. Supporters believe that these substances go through a process of transformation. For instance, in order to produce a solution of Arnica $6\times$, you mix one drop of arnica tincture in a bottle with nine drops of alcohol. You then shake this vigorously ten times. You take one drop of the resulting solution in that bottle, called Arnica $1\times$, mix it with nine drops of alcohol, and shake it ten times. The result is Arnica $2\times$. In order to produce a $6\times$ formula, you must repeat the same procedure in the same manner, using the same proportions, four more times. Since every individual step thins a solution by a factor of ten, the amount of the original substance in the final mixture is unbelievably small. Preparing a $12\times$ formula, for instance, is much like putting one drop of a substance in a big lake and then filling a bottle with water from the lake. Nevertheless, a $12\times$ medicine can be extremely effective. Shaking the substances at every step makes the difference!

Leeches live in shallow, brackish bodies of water. However, leeches used by practitioners and veterinarians are raised in laboratories and shipped on demand.

TIP

The art in homeopathy consists of choosing the proper medication and knowing the proper doses. A homeopathic physician must be able to understand an illness in all its complexity, which, in the case of an animal, is even more complicated since it can't talk. For that reason, you should refrain from treating your sick animal yourself; consult a licensed practitioner when your cat is sick.

Used as drops, Bach flower remedies come in small bottles. Some of the flowers need to be collected on particular days and at particular times of the day and then prepared according to specific instructions.

Practitioners use homeopathic medications to give injections. They also suspend the medications in alcohol and use them as drops. In addition, they use small pear-shaped pellets made from milk sugar and a prepared solution. Homeopathic medications also come in salve form.

Mobilization Therapy

Practitioners often use mobilization therapy for chronic illnesses, particularly those of the skin, in which the body has lost its capacity to recognize the illness. The result is that the body fails to make any attempt to heal itself. The therapy involves injecting a highly diluted pathogen, similar to the one that has caused the illness, into the body. Hopefully, this will stimulate the body to heal itself by mobilizing its ability against the new attack and against the original illness.

Because this procedure puts a great deal of stress on the entire immune system, the patient's treatment should include measures that support the immune system.

Bach Flower Therapy

This therapy is the most controversial and the least accepted form of treatment among medical professionals. Dr. Edward Bach, a British physician, created the therapy in the early 1900s. He believed that every organic illness also had a psychological component. According to his hypothesis, if you remove the psychological problem, the organic symptoms will also go away. After decades of studying many, many plants and after conducting countless experiments on himself, he was able to rank 38 "flowers" according to their effects on different psychological symptoms and behaviors.

Bach flower preparations are made from whole flowers or parts of flowers and used as drops. Bach flower therapy is truly an art. It requires extensive education and training to choose the right combination of flowers for each individual medication.

Bach flower therapy depends entirely on experience. Scientists have found no explanation for how these flowers work or why no other combination can bring about the same results. However, experience has shown that in cases of shock and for difficulties in adjusting to new situations, this therapy produces astonishing results.

Compresses and Poultices

A poultice is nothing more than a simple, usually single-layered compress placed on the injured or painful part of the body. Of course, in real life this creates a problem because our patients seldom stand still for very long. You can use wet or dry compresses and, in many cases, alternate both. You can also soak wet compresses in medical solutions or herbal teas.

As a general rule you use cold, wet compresses for acute inflammation. For almost all other conditions use warm, wet compresses. You usually use dry and warm compresses for prolonged therapies. An ice bag is an example of a dry, cold compress. Only use a cold compress for a short time, about five minutes. You might leave a warm, dry compress in place for about fifteen minutes.

Since compresses and poultices should provide comfort for the patient, use them gently and without force.

Organ Therapy

Although widely accepted in professional circles, this form of therapy is not well known among the lay population. It is somewhat similar to mobilization therapy, but the substances that go into the medication are unusual. For instance, the therapy uses colon bacteria (*Escherichia coli*), pyogenic organisms (*Staphylococcus aureus*), decaying meat (*Pyrogenia*), and certain organ tissues. These are suspended in homeopathically prepared medications of different strengths and injected into the patient. While a great uncertainty exists about the way this method works, the applicability is very great. Some practitioners have achieved astounding results, particularly in cases of arthritis.

Autotransfusion

Since this method calls for taking blood from the patient, practitioners don't use it very often for small animals. In cases where the patient's own defense mechanism needs to be mobilized, the practitioner takes a small amount of blood from the patient and then immediately injects it in a muscle. In special cases, the practitioner may add oxygen to the

TIP

Many of the compresses that we use on ourselves we can also use on animals. You can find more detailed information under "Nursing Care: Caring for an Ill Cat," pages 82 to 92.

13

Marigold (orange flowers) and chamomile flowers are surely two of the most well-known and most useful healing herbs. Borage (blue flowers) is useful for injuries, garlic is effective when used internally and for skin problems, and dried blueberries are very helpful in case of diarrhea.

blood, use ultraviolet rays on the blood, or use medication to fortify the blood before injecting it back into the patient. If, on the other hand, the practitioner wants to weaken the patient's immune system, he removes a larger amount of blood. He makes the decision to reinject part of the withdrawn blood on a case-by-case basis. Taking larger amounts of blood often serves to relieve stress on the heart. In such cases, the practitioner doesn't return the blood to the patient's body.

Herbal Therapy

In its basic form, herbal therapy is surely one of the oldest healing methods in medicine. Herbal therapy makes use of the healing properties of plants. Since nature's garden has an herb for every illness, you can use herbal therapy in almost all cases. This is especially true because you can use numerous healing plants in many different ways and for many different situations. For instance,

you may have the chamomile taken orally, but you can also use it for compresses and for inhalations. You can inject chamomile extract or use it in a healing salve.

Ozone Therapy

Ozone, a special form of oxygen, is a gas that has strong oxidation properties and changes easily into "normal" oxygen. In high concentrations, ozone has a very strong odor and is very poisonous. For treatment purposes, you use ozone in several different ways. One is to expose certain parts of the body to the gas, for example, in the treatment of persistent infections of mites, to kill the parasites. You may also use this therapy to treat blood that you have extracted before reinjecting it into the patient. This increases the body's own defense mechanism (see "Autotransfusion," page 13) and helps to combat viral infections. To make use of the antibacterial property of ozone, you can also add it to olive oil to help treat wounds that are difficult to heal.

Acupuncture

This ancient Chinese healing method assumes an imbalance in the flow of energy that influences or causes every illness afflicting an organism. By stimulating very specific points (the acupuncture points) through the skin, the practitioner can reestablish the normal flow of energy. The classical form of acupuncture uses very thin needles made from silver or gold. Recently, acupuncturists have begun to use a laser beam instead of needles. They also use acupuncture points as the sites for injecting medications, vitamins, and enzyme preparations.

Acupuncture can be helpful in many different conditions, including illnesses affecting internal organs, the blood, the nervous system, and for the relief of pain. An experienced acupuncturist can eliminate pain so completely that he can perform operations without anesthesia.

To know and be able to use the countless specific acupuncture points precisely during treatment is a high art. In large measure, success depends on the expertise and experience of the acupuncturist. Since the training and education for this healing art is very long and involved, only a few practitioners use acupuncture, and the ones who do usually use it only in uncomplicated cases.

This drawing shows the most important acupuncture points for cats. When you stimulate these points with thin needles similar to those used in classical Chinese acupuncture, you can influence the functioning of the internal organs. Some practitioners use a laser beam instead of needles.

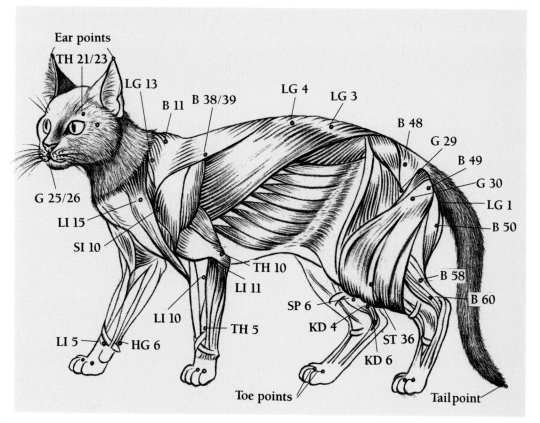

Ear points
TH 21/23
LG 13
B 11 B 38/39
LG 4 LG 3
B 48
G 29
B 49
G 30
LG 1
B 50
G 25/26
LI 15
SI 10
TH 10
LI 11
B 58
B 60
SP 6
LI 10
KD 4
TH 5
ST 36
LI 5 HG 6
KD 6
Toe points
Tail point

1. Medication

Note: Five drops equal one tablet or five to six pellets. You can purchase medications and salves at a health-food store.

Apis 4×
Homeopathic medication made from bee venom. In case of allergic reaction to insect bite, give one tablet every ten minutes.

Arnica
As a diluted solution (arnica tincture in 1:100 ratio diluted in water) or as a salve for compresses in all cases of nonbleeding injuries, such as strains and sprains.

At a strength of 4× or 6×, a homeopathic remedy for any injury: five drops every hour until symptoms improve, then three times a day.

Blueberry (dried form)
As a powder, mixed into food. Brings quick and effective relief for diarrhea.

Borage
Use in the form of compresses for every type of injury. Helps to stop bleeding and inflammation. For a compress, boil 3.5oz (100g) of borage roots in 1qt (1l) of water for ten minutes.

Calendula (common or pot marigold)
Used as a medicine for almost everything that ails us and our cats.

As an oil, for the treatment of ear mites and ear infections.

As a diluted solution from a tincture, for insect bites or ear infections.

Natural Healing Remedies

As a tea, for inhalation for respiratory problems.

Chamomile
As a tea, for stomach and intestinal problems and for inhalation in case of respiratory problems.

Added to the bath, for skin problems.

As a diluted solution from tincture, use for compresses for poorly healing wounds.

Coltsfoot
As a tea (using the flowers as well as the leaves), for inhalation for respiratory problems. As an expectorant, has infection-fighting properties, relieving many types of coughs when tea is used for inhalation several times a day.

Echinacea
Substances made from the *Echinacea angustifolia* flower, which grows wild in North America.

As a salve, for wounds that won't heal.

As drops, for infectious diseases and to stimulate the body's own healing power.

Garlic
In form of tablets, granules, or cloves (crushed), add to food. Effective against all parasitic, fungal, and skin diseases. (Garlic is not a substitute for regular treatment against worms!)

Indian Nerve Tea
Can buy ready-made to mix with

in Your Medicine Cabinet

food and add to drinking water in all cases of kidney and bladder problems.

Kaopectate

As a liquid, a ready-made preparation for diarrhea. Give your cat ½ to 2 teaspoons (2 to 10ml), depending on weight, up to five times a day.

Nux vomica 6 ×

A homeopathic medication used to control vomiting. Start with one tablet every hour, then try two tablets three times a day.

Important: Do not give to a pregnant cat.

Paraffin Oil

Clear oil made from the residues of oil-refining process. Often used as a base for salves. For constipation, mix approximately .5 teaspoon (2ml) in with food.

Peppermint

As a tea, for inhalation for respiratory problems and as a drink for stomach problems.

Rescue Remedy

A Bach flower remedy. As drops, for any type of shock. Give three drops every five minutes. Can also apply to the skin. Best place to apply is between the ears.

Traumeel

As a tablet, for any kind of injury. Give several times during the day. Consists of several different homeopathic remedies and *Echinacea*.

Veratrum album 4 ×

A homeopathic medication made from sprouted wheat, a plant belonging to the lily family that grows in the Alps. In North America the variety is known as American white hellebore, *Veratum viride*. Stimulates the circulatory system.

As a tablet, for acute failure of the circulatory system. Give one tablet (best if crushed), repeat after ten minutes.

2. Other Aids

Thermometer

Scissors

Elastic, plastic, and tube bandages

Disinfectant

A cotton blanket and a wool sock from which the tip has been cut off to use as a compress

Several disposable syringes (without the needles) to hold ½ teaspoon (2ml) and 4 teaspoons (20ml) to administer teas and other liquid medications

A blanket or other piece of cloth for keeping the animal warm or for transporting a severely injured or very sick animal; also used as an aid during the treatment of particularly difficult patients

A hot-water bottle or electric heating pad

TIP

In cases of discomfort or illness, always support a therapy with the appropriate diet (see "Diets," p. 88).

17

Developmental Stages of a Young Cat

TIP

Keep pregnant cats indoors one week before they are due to give birth. Many mothers-to-be have picked the neighbors' basement or shed as the place to birth their kittens.

Without a doubt, kittens are among the most adorable babies in the animal world. Most people find that they can't be angry with these little creatures even if, as is the case with "children," they get themselves in all sorts of trouble during their exploratory phase and later, when they are adolescents. Every good and bad experience a cat has during this time sets the stage for the rest of its life. Experiences during this phase also determine whether or not a cat will trust people or become suspicious and shy.

From Birth to the Fifth Day

A cat's pregnancy usually lasts between fifty-eight and sixty-two days; but, just as

with humans, variations of a few days either way are normal, and a particular breed may have a range that differs from the general statistics (e.g., Siamese, as much as seventy-one days is normal).

Most births take place at night or during the early-morning hours. Generally speaking, the whole event proceeds without complications. The only exception occurs when the mother has more than five kittens or is very young. In these cases, she needs help from us.

In most instances, you will find four or five little kittens in the nest. Of course, single births are also possible, as are litters of eight or nine.

Kittens are still "unfinished" little creatures at birth. Biologically, they are "nestlings." They are deaf, blind, and toothless, and their legs are much too weak to use. They cuddle together in their nest, totally dependent on their mother. Their mother's warmth is the most vital ingredient for their survival, because they are not yet able to regulate their own body temperature. The reason

Above: Kittens are typical "nestlings," which means that they are completely dependent on their mother for food, protection, and warmth.

Right: After a kitten has emerged, the mother cat frees it from the birth sack and licks it dry. This sets the circulatory system in motion.

they cuddle so close together in the nest is to keep themselves warm.

At birth, a healthy kitten weighs between 3oz and 4oz (80gm and 120gm). Male kittens are usually a little heavier than their sisters. However, determining the sex of a kitten is only possible by inspecting its hind quarters: the distance between the anus and the round opening that later develops into sex organs is longer in males. In females, the opening is more oval and located closer to the anus.

The first milk that the mother cat produces is colostrum. This milk is high in nutrients and contains very important immune substances that give kittens protection against infectious diseases.

Very quickly, each kitten establishes its favorite nipple. It will defend its nipple against intrusion by other siblings. Newborn kittens spend their first few days "attached" to a nipple. They gain

about ½oz (15gm) every day. The mother cat will lick the belly and anus of her kittens frequently to stimulate excretion, which at this age is strictly a reflex action. Without this "massaging," the kittens wouldn't be able to discharge any excretion at all. During the first two to

The Runt of the Litter

Sometimes a litter contains one particularly weak kitten who has little chance of claiming a good nipple. The result is a vicious cycle in which this kitten grows even weaker and becomes even less able to fight for itself. If the mother cat lives outside or on a farm, this kitten, called the runt of the litter, usually does not make it. But if the mother is a house cat and you can support the runt with supplemental feedings, it has a good chance of developing normally. Natural supplements (ask your health practitioner) stimulate the immune system and are very helpful in strengthening the kitten's self-defense mechanism. You feed the supplements to the kitten with a disposable syringe (without the needle, of course). For more on this subject see "Case Histories: General Susceptibility to Infections," page 33.

four days after birth, the mother cat cares for her kittens around the clock, almost never leaving the next.

If a mother cat does not care for her young—which is very rare—or if the mother cat dies in an accident, only a foster mother or "wet nurse" can save the kittens.

People who try to raise kittens that are less than three weeks old face a fairly hopeless undertaking. Medications are of little help. Fortunately, most mother cats have such a well-developed mothering instinct that they will be more than willing to care for kittens that are not their own.

Fifth Day to Third Week

At the earliest, a kitten begins to open its eyes on the fifth day, but in general, this doesn't happen until the eighth to fourteenth day. The first sign is a small slit above the corner of the nose that slowly opens up all by itself during the next two to three days. However, the kitten still cannot see. Another two to three days must pass after the eyes are completely open before they will react to light or movement. A kitten's ability to see increases steadily over the next few weeks. The process of acquiring hearing takes place at the same time.

In the first week, kittens move short distances by pulling themselves about with their front legs. Towards the end of the second week, they will try to stand up or walk. Most of the time, however, these attempts amount to no more than a crawl, because their tummies are too heavy to lift off the ground for any length of time.

Fourth to Eighth Week

Now the kittens are becoming more and more ambulatory. They start climbing out of the nest and begin to explore their immediate environment. Whenever the kittens are not nursing or sleeping, they are busy improving their physical abilities. In the beginning, they look rather

Kittens begin to open their eyes between the eighth and fourteenth day. Their first teeth appear around the twelfth day. Kittens will make their first attempts at standing and crawling when they are only two weeks old.

clumsy walking, climbing, and jumping, but they continue undeterred. They are now able to retract their claws and, when necessary, expose them again. The kittens also begin to groom themselves vigorously, even if they eventually loose their balance and fall flat on their face. Thank goodness for their mother's tongue. She uses it just like a washcloth.

When they leave their nest to explore their environment, they stay away longer and longer and move farther and farther away. By the time kittens are four to five weeks old, they know the whole room that is their nursery, and they always find their way back to the nest, no matter where they have been. Kittens also begin to pay attention to each other more and more. They play and roughhouse only to turn around and lick each other or cuddle up next to each other.

During the second to seventh week, every experience the kittens have, with people or with one of their own, leaves a lasting impression on them. This means that if kittens have positive and intensive contacts with people before they are seven weeks old, they will usually grow up to become people-friendly family cats as adults.

By now, the kittens have gained a lot of weight. By the end of the first month, they will have quadrupled their birth weight. However, their strenuous climbing and running stretches them out.

During this time, it becomes obvious that the mother won't be able to produce enough milk to satisfy the appetite of all her offspring. When they are five or six weeks old, they will try to eat little bits of solid food. This is the first step in the weaning process. This is also the time when kittens start using the litter box. In general, they take to this invention rather quickly. In the beginning, however, sudden urges may often result in deposits of urine or stool in places other than the litter box, such as under the couch, for

Danger of Infection

During the time when kittens are beginning to take solid food and starting to explore their environment, their environment bombards them with all kinds of germs. And since their mother's milk now lacks the substances that supported their immune system, the kittens are vulnerable to infections. The minute a kitten shows the first symptom of illness (loss of appetite, apathy, diarrhea, or vomiting) you should take its temperature immediately. We discuss

how to do this in "Caring for an Ill Cat," pages 82 to 92. If the temperature is above 103°F (39.5°C) or below 99°F (37.8°C), consult your practitioner or veterinarian immediately. If the kitten's temperature is normal, 101°F (38.5°C), you might want to call the practitioner and ask for advice. Check out which remedies or diets you can use at home. (See "Natural Healing Remedies in Your Medicine Cabinet," page 16.) You'll find information about what symptoms to look for in "The Most Frequently Occurring Illnesses," on page 29.

Right: In general, kittens learn to use the litter box without any problems, although their scratching instinct might not be completely developed right away.

Left: Kittens usually start grooming themselves when they are four weeks old. Make sure that you comb and brush long-haired cats, because their own efforts are not enough to keep their fur in good shape.

instance. The kittens will eat more and more solid food until, by the eighth week, they are able to live entirely on solid food.

This, however, does not necessarily mean that mother's milk should be or will be drying up. In most cases, the mother cat will still allow her kittens to nurse now and then, primarily to develop a sense of security rather than to provide nourishment.

Ninth to Twelfth Week

At the beginning of the third month, kittens are beyond their "kindergarten" phase and are ready to start "first grade," so to speak. Nothing in their environment is safe from their relentless drive to explore. Siblings will chase each other

TIP

You should deworm kittens for the first time when they are four to five weeks old.

TIP

If the mother cat has a large litter or is a little weak, you may start to feed the kittens additional food when they are four weeks old. Gluten-free, pureed baby food, raw or cooked lean beef, or cooked and pureed chicken works best. Giving extra food to strong kittens leaves more of the mother's milk for the weaker kittens.

As early as four weeks old, kittens will try to taste their first mouthful from their mother's food bowl. By eight weeks they will exclusively seek nourishment from solid food.

with great passion and use wrestling games to develop endurance and savvy. With great enthusiam, they will look for all kinds of objects with which to practice catching and fighting. A crumbled piece of paper, little balls, or a cork from a wine bottle are wonderful toys that allow them to safely play their games. Mother cats living on a farm or outdoors now start bringing their prey home. Although they usually bring it home after they have killed it, sometimes they bring it home alive to teach their offspring how to catch and kill.

The mother cat now leaves the nest more often and for longer periods of time. She still grooms her kittens' fur, and she remains a patient teacher and playmate. Kittens show more and more of their individual characteristics. Some develop into fearless fighters; others are timid and careful; and some kittens are fun-loving bundles of affection. Keep these different characteristics in mind when you look for a new home for your kittens.

Parasites

If you allow your kitten to go outside, instead of restricting it to your house or apartment, be prepared for parasites. When a kitten eats ferociously and still loses weight, it usually has caught either spool worms or tapeworms. Your practitioner can easily handle such parasites with natural remedies. You can find out more about this in the section "Case Histories: Severe Parasite Infestations," on page 37.

You may also have to treat external parasites, such as fleas or ear mites. Once the parasites are gone, make sure to check your kitten frequently and treat the kitten immediately if you see any evidence of a recurrence or of a new infestation.

And this brings us to the subject of having to say good-bye. At the earliest,

Kittens learn by playing with their siblings and with different objects. Without such activities, it would be impossible for a kitten to develop its true personality.

Left: Even on an early-morning outing, the mother stays close, continually available to the kittens.

kittens go to their new homes when they are eight weeks old. Actually they do better if you wait until they are twelve weeks old. Before they leave, they must get their first shot: the very first, basic immunization against feline leukemia. We discuss the immunizations necessary to protect cats on page 26. If possible, don't give all of the kittens away at once. Instead, give them away over a period of one or two weeks. The extra time makes the separation easier for the mother cat and also helps to prevent inflammation of her nipples. By the way, your practitioner or veterinarian is usually a good source if you are looking for a kitten.

Fourth to Fifth Month

Often, a kitten is three, sometimes even four months old before it goes to a new home. This means that the kitten has to get used to totally new smells and sounds and fit itself into a new family situation.

If, however, the members of the new family interact enthusiastically and lovingly, a kitten of that age seldom has a problem with being homesick. A kitten is now at the stage where it spends the whole day exploring its world, and, of

TIP

If your pet will have to spend a lot of time alone, you might want to take home two kittens because one might be bored and frustrated by itself.

TIP

During the time when permanent teeth begin to erupt, give your kitten a leather bone (available in pet stores) or a piece of cartilage from bone. This might distract the kitten from chewing dangerous objects, such as electrical cords.

A cat can be a wonderful companion for a school-age child. A child who is around a cat learns to respect the personality of another individual, in addition to learning how to take responsibility for its well-being.

course, eating, sleeping, and playing with you.

During these months, kittens are often a little out of sorts. They chew on all kinds of things, always looking for hard objects. The reason is clear: they are getting their permanent teeth. Unlike humans, cats do not have a gap where a milk or baby tooth has fallen out. A kitten's permanent teeth appear next to the ones they are replacing, which means that for a few days a young cat has two sets of teeth. As soon as the permanent tooth is large enough to function, the baby tooth falls out. In most cases, the kitten simply swallows the tooth. During this time, a kitten's gums are often swollen and inflamed. Some kittens even have a slight fever and mild diarrhea when they are cutting a new tooth.

If you have not had your kitten immunized, you need to have this done immediately.

Immunization Schedule for Cats

Eighth to Tenth Week
First shot for feline leukemia

Twelfth Week
Second shot for feline leukemia
First shot for feline catarrh ("flu")

Sixteenth Week
Second shot for feline catarrh
Shot for cat distemper

Every Year
Booster shot for cat catarrh and distemper

Every Two Years
Booster shot for feline leukemia
Some regions require regular, periodic rabies vaccination (check with your veterinarian)

Immunization against feline catarrh ("flu") is not totally foolproof because the shot is only effective against two of the causes. Check your cat's eyes regularly for discharge, as recommended in the "Health Checklist" on page 81. You'll find a discussion on how to treat cat catarrh with natural methods in "Case Histories" on page 30.

Dangers

For clumsy or inexperienced cats, houses are full of dangers. Falls and poisonings poise the biggest risks. People don't realize how many things in their homes can be dangerous for kittens and for older cats. For instance, kittens and cats can find cigarettes, medications, fertilizers for house plants, cleaning solutions, other chemicals, and poisonous house plants, such as ficus, ivy, and dieffenbachia. In addition, electrical cords, hot stoves, and windows that open by tilting or that are left open all too often cause injuries. Without thinking, you can step on a kitten's paw or close a door on its tail. Because a kitten's body is still very supple and heals rather quickly, such accidents usually do not have the dire consequences of those mentioned above.

For an injured cat, use Bach flower Rescue Remedy, a medication that has proven to be very effective in cases of shock. It is most effective if you give the injured cat two to three drops every five minutes in the ears or by mouth. For further information about first aid and how to use it, see "First Aid," pages 93 to 95. We discuss how your veterinarian or practitioner treats injuries in his office in "Case Histories" on pages 34 to 36.

Immunization against feline leukemia is not one-hundred-percent effective either. If you are going to have your cat immunized against this illness, it is imperative that your veterinarian or practitioner do a leukemia test first.

Cats with access to the outside have a chance to practice hunting and territorial behavior.

Sixth to Twelfth Month

This is the period of puberty. At its conclusion, your kitten is fully developed sexually.

Profound changes in the hormone levels accompany puberty and sexual maturity. The first sign is restlessness and, for some cats, a few "accidents," meaning that they don't get to their litter box in time. Female cats reach sexual maturity when they come into heat for the first time, usually between the eighth and tenth month, but no later than one year. A female cat in heat will start to roll around on the ground and become very vocal. It will literally "call" for a mate. As a rule, female cats come into heat two to three times a year. However, if she has not mated, the whole scenario will start all over again in three to four weeks. In extreme cases, this behavior becomes permanent.

TIP

Protect open windows and balconies with screens. Windows that open by tilting are dangerous. A cat that gets caught in one may sustain fatal injuries in an attempt to free itself

27

A cat in heat can be a real challenge. If you do not intend to breed your cat, have it neutered as soon as possible.

TIP

Have your cat tattooed. Animal shelters can trace cats with tattoos to their owners and easily return them.

Puberty lasts much longer for males than for female cats. Sex hormones begin to develop when males are only four months old. They often start to "practice" on a female cat when they are six to eight months old. Successful mating, however, occurs only after the ninth to twelfth month. The average age is nine months. Sexually mature male cats have a very annoying habit: They mark their territory by spraying urine that contains a special secretion from the anal glands. This has a very unpleasant odor to humans. Unfortunately for the owner, an indoor cat's territory is the entire indoor area.

These unpleasant behaviors from both male and female cats are some of the reasons why we should neuter our cats. Of course, a principal reason is the overwhelming number of strays that wind up in animal shelters. We should feel compelled to help curb the unwanted proliferation of our pets.

One-year-old cats are sexually mature and almost "grown up," but they have not yet joined the ranks of adults. Their be-

Neutering

Castration, usually thought of in relation to males, simply means that the surgeon removes the gonads. In a female animal that means the removal of the ovaries and frequently the uterus; in a male animal, the surgeon removes the testicles. Since the gonads produce sexual hormones, this form of neutering not only prevents reproduction, but also eliminates the sexual drive. This surgery also stops the spraying by males and the incessant rolling of females. Another neutering surgical procedure is spaying, in which the veterinary surgeon ties the female's fallopian tubes or the male's vas deferens. The drawback of spaying is that it doesn't affect the heat cycle of the female or the undesirable behavior of the male. For both forms of neutering, your pet comes home in one to two days (have a tattoo identification mark done at the same time). A visit to the vet may be in order about a week later to assess progress and remove stitches. In about a month the fur will grow back.

havior is still kittenlike, and they are still full of mischief. They still love to romp around and play wild games of chase and catch, even if not as often as they did a few months earlier. Engaging in playful behavior is particularly important for single indoor cats that do not have a chance to frolic outdoors. Owners of indoor cats must provide opportunities and activities for their cats to be fit.

The Most Frequently Occurring Illnesses

Recognizable Symptoms	Possible Reasons	What You Can Do	See Your Veterinarian
Limping; limb sensitive to touch; possible loss of appetite and apathy	Sprain, fracture, torn ligaments due to an accident; burn injury, beginning abscess; less likely, a viral infection	Use cold arnica compresses; look for open wounds or old scabs; give Traumeel tablets: at first, every hour, then four times a day; take temperature	If the cat can't move the limb at all on its own; won't allow touch; when there are large open wounds; if temperature is above 103°F (39.5°C)
Bumps (pliable or hard and swollen), possibly accompanied by loss of appetite and sensitivity to touch	Abscess; tumors (not painful)	Use compresses with healing earth; give tablespoon of Traumeel three to four times a day; give *Hepar sulfuris* 8× to let an abscess ripen, then give 12× twice a day for a week	In any case to establish proper diagnosis (to determine if it is an abscess or a tumor)
Constant shaking of the head; constant scratching of one or both ears; tilting the head to the side; black or brown substance inside the ears	Ear mites	Apply oxygenated olive oil into the ear canal and the base of the ear for one week; if infestation is light, use Rose-of-Sharon, or baby oil	Usually not necessary
Frequent overall, incessant scratching and licking; obvious severe itching	Fleas, lice (when attached to fur, their eggs can be mistaken for dandruff)	Check fur carefully; if fleas are present, comb with flea comb and use flea powder; repeat treatment after three days; treat surroundings; give garlic	If no parasites can be detected or if a severe skin inflammation has developed
Constant sleeping; does not play; eats little or not at all; possibly inflamed throat and loose baby teeth	Beginning infection or infection already in progress; tonsillitis	Take temperature; observe animal closely; give defense-stimulating medication, such as *Echinacea*; for sore throat, use throat compresses	If no improvement in two days; if temperature is above 103°F (39.5°C) or below 100°F (37.8°C)
Vomiting usually accompanied by apathy and loss of appetite	Upset stomach due to food or to poisoning by poisonous plants in house or garden; infection (feline leukemia); intestinal blockage due to swallowed foreign object	Take temperature; do not feed for ten hours; give only peppermint tea; give defense-stimulating medication such as *Echinacea*; if improvement continues, feed a light diet for one week	If temperature is above 103°F (39.5°C) or below 100°F (37.8°C); when vomiting continuously; animal becomes weak; diarrhea or no bowl movement for more then twenty-four hours; no improvement after two days
Diarrhea, usually accompanied by apathy and loss of appetite	Parasite infestation of the intestinal tract, usually by spool or tapeworms; infectious disease (feline leukemia); poisoning, often from poisonous plants or from eating mice that have been poisoned	Take temperature; do not feed for ten hours; give only fennel and chamomile tea; give defense-stimulating medications, such as *Echinacea*; give one teaspoon of Kaopectate several times a day; after diarrhea clears, feed a light diet for three days	If no improvement within two days; temperature is above 103°F or (39.5°C) or below 100°F (37.8°C); other symptoms appear

Case Histories from My Practice

Feline catarrh ("flu") often attacks kittens in the first year of their lives. The initial signs of this very dangerous illness are fever and a yellow discharge from the eyes and nose.

Feline Catarrh ("Flu")

Because several different viruses cause feline catarrh, it is not one distinct illness. Veterinarians often refer to it as feline catarrh complex. While different symptoms can affect different organs, the majority affect the upper respiratory tract, the nose, and the throat. The flu-like illness usually begins with frequent sneezing, a clear and then yellow discharge from the eyes and nose, and a fever of 104°F (40°C). Some cases are so severe that yellow pus covers the kitten's fur and eyes, and its gums are so inflamed that the kitten refuses to eat or drink, further weakening its system and leading to dehydration. Unless they receive treatment, sixty to eighty percent of all kittens with this illness will not survive. Those that do survive usually carry the effects of the disease for the rest of their lives.

Not long ago, I examined two little kittens in my office. Both showed all the symptoms of severe feline catarrh. The owner had picked the kittens up from a farm just two days before. Both kittens were in lamentable condition. A veterinarian had already prescribed antibiotics and had dewormed them.

We proceeded to give the kittens an injection of an immune-stimulating herbal medication every other day. I also advised the owner to administer cham-

Ten days later, we stopped the injections, using the same medication in tablet form. We gave the immune-stimulating medication in the form of a paste. After four more days, we also discontinued the inhalations. The ulcers in and around the kittens' mouths had healed enough for them to eat without difficulty, and their eyes were again bright and clear. It took a total of three weeks for both kittens to become completely healthy.

As soon as kittens are old enough, the mother cat will take them on frequent outings, allowing them to explore their surroundings. The first such experience is particularly exciting: new things, new smells, and new sounds are everywhere. Unfortunately, for some kittens this is no fun at all because they are suffering from pollen allergies.

omile inhalation twice a day and to treat the infected eyes and the ulcers in and around the mouths with a warm chamomile solution, followed by cold chamomile compresses for the eyes.

Pollen Allergies

More and more people suffer from pollen allergies, but few people know that cats, too, can have allergic reactions to pollen.

In the beginning, the symptoms are very much like those of feline catarrh ("flu").

One morning at the end of April, a worried cat owner called to tell me one of her four-week old kittens suddenly had a severe discharge from its eyes and was sneezing constantly. The kitten had no other symptoms, and its appetite was fine.

During the course of the conversation, the owner recalled that the symptoms seemed to coincide with the first time the kitten went outside. In addition, the owner said she had opened every window in her house to let the fresh, spring air into the house. We decided to wait and see and to keep a close eye on the kitten for the next few days. And indeed, all the symptoms disappeared overnight when she kept the cat inside. The symptoms did not return until a few days later, when the kittens went outside again. These observations strongly suggested

Often one kitten among the litter is weaker than the rest. Supplementing its food can make up for any initial shortcomings. Supplemental feedings for all kittens are helpful if the litter is very large or if the mother is very young and weak.

Feline Infectious Peritonitis (FIP)

Feline Infectious Peritonitis (also known as FIP) is a fatal disease caused by a virus, and feared by all cat owners and breeders. At this time, no immunization is available to prevent it.

A cat with FIP stops eating and loses weight rapidly. It usually has a type of diarrhea for which there is no effective medication. The cat continues to lose ground, becoming weaker and weaker. The belly becomes extended and pear-shaped due to an accumulation of fluids. Fluid can also accumulate in the lungs, causing the cat to have trouble breathing. (In so-called dry FIP, no fluid accumulates.) We diagnose the illness through X rays and palpitation. A blood test may be helpful because an infected cat always shows antibodies in the blood, as well as a change in the blood and protein chemistry.

If we detect the illness early, we can use medications that may delay the sad, inevitable end. In most cases, the infected cat dies within a few weeks. A practitioner can only give short-term relief from this disease. Eventually, the cat has to be put to sleep.

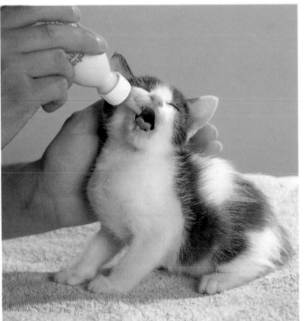

that the kitten had a pollen allergy.

The kitten came to my office for the next couple of days for acupuncture treatments that lessened the most acute symptoms. I treated the conjunctivitis with the homeopathic remedy *Euphrasia*, made from eyebright, a healing herb known for centuries. Obviously, the

owner should try to keep this cat indoors as much as possible to limit the exposure to allergy-causing agents. Since the owner was planning to find new homes for all of the kittens when they were twelve weeks old, I suggested that she give this particular kitten to someone looking for an indoor cat and that she inform the new owner of the kitten's problems with allergies.

General Susceptibility to Infections

Frequently, one kitten is weaker than the rest of the litter. For no apparent reason, it never seems to gain much ground.

Because it is weaker, it always loses in the search for the best nipple, and therefore, it doesn't get enough milk.

Such a runt came to my office when it was sixteen weeks old. Leni's owner complained that this kitten was always sickly. As soon as she had gotten over a bout with diarrhea, she came down with a sore throat, and then she had some other infection. Her appetite was poor, and her favorite activity was sleeping on the warm radiator. On the rare occasions when Leni played at all, she did so with a short burst of energy, always collapsing, totally exhausted, afterwards. The owner's veterinarian, who had done some blood and stool tests, had ruled out any internal problems or parasite infections. The veterinarian also discounted loneliness and boredom as reasons for her lethargy because the kitten always

During the period when kittens are switching from nursing to solid food, they are very susceptible to infectious diseases of all kinds. Bouts with diarrhea are not uncommon at this time.

A kitten is constantly developing and sometimes exploring beyond her capabilities. The startled kitten may fall but not be hurt. Kittens enthusiastically learn to scramble, climb, and balance, and from time to time overestimate their skills and tumble from a tree or bookcase.

had company in the house, including people and a male kitten from the same litter.

The kitten was very delicate, but I could not detect any signs of illness. She seemed to be rather shy and fearful but not unfriendly towards people. In homeopathy, all these symptoms taken together point to a medical condition to be treated with phosphorus (a chemical element that burns quickly and forcefully and goes out just as fast). I decided to administer a dose of high-potency phosphorus, which I repeated one week later. In addition, the kitten was given an immune-stimulating herbal extract as well as a combination Bach flower remedy. I advised the owner to give both to the kitten several times a day.

Leni came back three weeks later. She had obviously grown, and her weight gain was rather remarkable. Her owner reported that she was much more lively, slept less, and was not as shy or anxious.

No new infections had occurred since her last visit. Two weeks later, we decided to discontinue all medication. Today, two years later, Leni is still a delicate cat, but she is healthy, and her body is able to defend itself against illnesses.

Injuries from Falls and Accidents

Just like children, young cats are full of curiosity. They are adventurous when exploring their world. Unfortunately, this makes them prone to accidents, because they lack experience and physical control. Falls and burns occur frequently.

Feline Panleukopenia (FPK, also called Feline Infectious Enteritis)

Feline Panleukopenia, incorrectly called feline "distemper," is a highly infectious viral disease often contracted by young cats. All bodily secretions (saliva, urine, stool) spread the disease. The virus can remain alive outside the body for as long as eight months. In addition to spreading from cat to cat, the infection can spread through feeding bowls, cat carriers, and sleeping quarters. People can even transmit it on the soles of shoes they wear outside. The incubation period is four to six days after infection. The condition worsens within hours. Without treatment, eighty to ninety percent of all infected cats under the age of ten weeks will not survive. Cats younger than four weeks have no chance at all of survival.

Because of the rapid progression of the disease, early detection dictates the outcome. In my practice, we have successfully treated infected cats with natural remedies and intensive care.

Such a misfortune happened to Max, a little male cat, who had obviously overestimated his abilities while climbing. Max's owner described him as being particularly lively and inquisitive. Two days before I saw him, he had attempted to climb a large yucca palm. After reaching the top, he became frightened and tried to turn around. The owner saw what was happening but was unable to prevent the little guy from falling. However, because Max immediately began running, showing no outward signs of injuries, she thought things had worked out satisfactorily. Sadly, the next day Max was limping very badly. During the examination, one paw was very sensitive to the touch. However, he had no problem moving about, even if his movements were somewhat limited, and it seemed as if he had not broken any bones. I asked the owner to use cold compresses and prescribed Traumeel tablets. In addition, we exposed the paw to magnet therapy every other day. Healing proceeded quickly, and a week later, the little guy was as lively and curious as ever.

Mira, a five-month-old kitten, had jumped on a hot burner on the stove— another example of the trials of youthful inexperience. In spite of the fact that the owner put the kitten's paws in cold water, by the next morning, huge blisters had developed. She had seriously burned all five pads on one front paw and three on one hind paw. Obviously, blisters on the paws can burst easily, posing a danger of infection, unless we bandage them immediately. However we must also pay attention to the effects of the shock that the

Falling out of windows or off of balconies is not unusual, particularly for indoor cats. Cats who have access to the outdoors face different, but no less dangerous, situations from cars and other animals. Outdoor cats are also more prone to parasite infestations, which can truly be a problem.

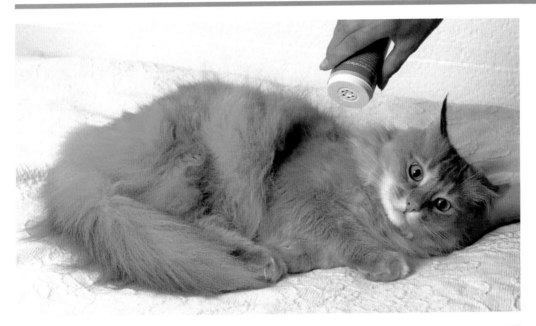

Above: If you detect fleas, treat your cat with flea powder and use a flea comb.

Left: Fleas are not easy to detect. They disappear with lightning speed as soon as you start examining the cat's fur.

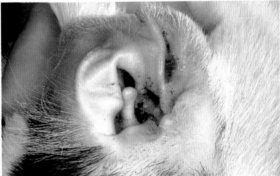

Right: Because ear mites are parasites that are frequent guests, you need to check your cat's ears on a regular basis. A light infestation is easy to treat.

patient has suffered. The Bach flower Rescue Remedy, a proven treatment for all types of shock, was the medication of choice. I gave the kitten an injection of Traumeel to lessen the pain and to stimulate the body's own defense mechanism. Finally, we bandaged the injured paws, using a thick layer of calendula salve to prevent the bandages from sticking to the open wounds. We changed the bandages every day. In addition, we gave Mira the homeopathic medication, arnica 4×, four times a day.

After three days, the wounds on the hind paw had practically healed. The front paw, more seriously injured, took longer to heal. In fact, ten days passed before we no longer needed to bandage it.

Severe Parasite Infestations

Cats with access to the outdoors will always pick up parasites, from infested prey or from other cats. While a few of these pests won't create a serious health hazard, a severe infestation can weaken a cat's constitution and can cause grave health problems. Young cats particularly are in danger if they have not yet developed the necessary resistance.

We distinguish between external parasites, such as fleas and ear mites, and internal parasites that turn up in the intestinal tract, in muscles, or even in the blood. The most frequently occurring intestinal parasites are tapeworms and spool worms. These cause constant weight loss and a steadily increasing appetite.

Not long ago, the owner of a male cat with a severe case of infestation walked into my office. The cat was about eight weeks old and had been found in a shopping center, emaciated and terribly weak. The cat was a truly sad sight: its body was crawling with fleas, and such a massive black crust (typical of ear-mite infestation) covered its ears that I was sure the little guy had lost much of his ability to hear. As I palpitated his belly, the otherwise lethargic kitten cried out in pain. However, I could not detect any external injuries or obvious acute problems.

My first course of action was to give him Bach Flower Rescue Remedy, which he accepted without protest. I also gave him an injection of a vitamin-enriched electrolyte solution to strengthen his weakened system. After I cleaned his ears with oxygenated olive oil, we went to work on the fleas with flea powder and a flea comb.

Only two hours later, the little patient was much less lethargic. Although he was still rather unsteady, he got up, began to eat, and even started to groom himself. By the next day, he had improved greatly and showed lively interest in the rest of the cats in his new surroundings. We dewormed him, treating the mild case of diarrhea that followed with a special diet (see "Diet," pages 88 to 89). Within a few days, the diarrhea was gone. Over the next four weeks, we used *abrotanum* (wormwood) 1× to continue the deworming process. Three days after I admitted him, I decided to end his quarantine, allowing him to interact with the rest of the cat population. He was free of parasites within two and a half weeks and had gained 7oz (200g). Thanks to a special diet, within four weeks his physical development was where it should be. He turned into a healthy, lively, and wonderfully mischievous little rascal.

Tapeworms are parasites that frequently afflict cats. Sometimes, the individual pieces, shown here, are connected. Dried-up pieces of tapeworm look very much like rice.

The Lifestyle of Cats

A kitten becomes an adult cat between the ages of twelve and sixteen months. Only the proportions of the body and the way the animal moves change; the cat becomes quieter and more sure of itself. Youthful enthusiasm gives way to regal poise, at least most of the time. The constant need to look for new adventures and discoveries—a driving force until now—gives way to a more routine and

predictable day. Cats are amazingly insistent that their owners respect their established eating, sleeping, and social times. These animals are truly creatures of habit! Sometimes they react so angrily to any break or change in their daily routine that they develop behavioral problems or psychosomatic illnesses.

But if they can follow their routine, most cats are usually easy to care for. With proper food, plenty of opportunities for play, and, most important of all, tender loving attention from the owner, cats will be happy. Infectious diseases are seldom a problem at this age, particularly if the owner sticks to the immunization schedule (see "Immunization Schedule," page 26) and checks the cat's teeth as suggested (see "Health Examination," page 80).

A Cat's Body

When cats left the wild to become house pets many thousands of years ago, neither their body structure nor their physical abilities changed. Over time, breeders began to pay more attention to color and type of fur than to anything else, leaving intact the instincts that made them such perfect hunters, no matter how cuddly they might be.

Body Structure

Cats' supple bodies have more than five hundred surprisingly strong muscles. These enable them to approach their prey in almost total silence, jumping 6ft (2m) into the air from a sitting position and jumping up to 4ft (1.2m) in length. In close confrontations, cats are almost unbelievably agile.

Claws

Using special muscles, cats are able to extend their claws with lightning speed. While cats are at rest or sleeping, an intricate ligament mechanism keeps the

TIP

Check your cat's teeth once a week and have the tartar removed when necessary.

TIP

Outdoor cats sharpen their claws on tree trunks or wooden objects. To satisfy the sharpening instinct of indoor cats, the owner must supply a scratching carpet or a scratching post.

claws safely retracted in their sheathes. The claws of the front paws are sharp as needles. They are very effective weapons in a fight, and they are indispensable for climbing, as well as for catching and holding prey.

Fur

A cat's skin is very supple and "movable," like a loose, comfortable sweater. The suppleness is especially advantageous in close combat with a rival or with a prey that is fighting back, because it helps to confine most injuries to the skin, where they are usually superficial. In addition, fur protects a cat from the cold and the sun. It keeps injuries to a minimum and, to a limited degree, repels water. During the winter, outdoor cats grow a very dense and warm winter coat.

Eyes

Of all a cat's sensory organs, the eyes are by far the most developed and the most important organ for hunting. The eyes

Fleas

Fleas are the primary parasites that attack cats. Even cats with excellent grooming habits who spend a lot of time caring for their fur are unable to keep these pests at bay. For that reason, check your cat's fur every few days, particularly if it has access to the outside and, if necessary, use a flea comb and flea powder. In general, I do not recommend flea collars because of the poisonous substances they contain. Also, the collar might get caught, getting the cat in trouble.

are large and crystal clear. They never miss even the smallest movements. They still function perfectly with light six times weaker than the light level necessary for people. A cat's eyes have a layer of cells that function like a mirror, reflecting incoming light.

Ears

A cat's ears are far superior to those of human beings. A cat can hear a mouse walking almost silently across the floor and the faint peeping sounds the mouse makes. A cat can also determine with great precision where a sound is coming from. More than twenty muscles move each "radar screen," concentrating directly on the source of a sound. Cats are not only able to hear sounds that we cannot, they can also hear sounds with a much higher pitch than we can hear. While our maximum limit is frequencies of 20,000 hertz (cycles per second), cats can hear sounds up to 65,000 hertz.

Cats need their claws for climbing and hunting, but they also need them when confronting a rival. Meticulous grooming keeps the claws sharp and in good shape.

Olfactory Sense

Cats' sense of smell is also much stronger than a human's. Cats produce a "real" picture of the smells they encounter in their environment and the people in it. They will investigate strange people or strange cats with extensive sniffing. Foreign objects receive the same close examination. Cats won't eat food until they have thoroughly checked it out. They have an additional organ, somewhere between tasting and smelling, that human beings lack. This is the Jacobson organ, located at the roof of their palate. If a cat comes across a particularly interesting smell, it will suck the air surrounding the object so that it passes against this organ. The mouth opens slightly, and the upper lip pulls up.

Whiskers

Sometimes, we call a cat's long whiskers its "third eye." The whiskers, also called vibrissae, grow on the upper lip, the cheeks, the chin, above the eyes, and at the back and front of the legs. Several

nerve endings, located at the base of the whiskers, register every change in the position of each individual whisker. The whiskers are very effective antennae, helping the cat to squeeze through dark and narrow spaces or holes. They also enable a cat to "see" the outline of its prey in the dark.

Cat Talk

To properly care for and to interact with a cat, the owner has to understand its language. The following section will make it easier to distinguish between a cat's different sounds and expressions.

Well-Being

When a cat is happy, its whole body relaxes, and its tail points straight up. The eyes are calm, and depending on the light, the pupils are open. The whiskers are slightly spread out to the sides; the ears are upright and slightly turned to the sides.

No animals use their physical abilities better than cats do. Climbing, stretching to make themselves thinner, or, as in this case, balancing on a narrow pole is no problem for a cat. But in spite of their skills, accidents will occur because cats are not naturally accustomed to the buildings people construct.

TIP

You need to brush longhair cats every day.

TIP

Cats are very sensitive to shrill, high-pitched sounds. They particularly dislike noises in the high register. Try to protect your cat from such sounds.

Right: A cat's whiskers are extremely sensitive, tactile organs that function as antennae. The whiskers on the upper lip are especially interesting and well developed.

Right and left below: The pupils regulate the amount of incoming light, much as the shutter of a camera does. When the light is weak, the pupils are large and round; when the light is strong, the pupils turn into small slits.

Ear Mites

Ear mites cause almost all infections in the inner ear. A cat with ear mites will scratch constantly, often leading to dangerous infections. Check your cat's ears regularly (see "Health Checklist," page 81) so that you can detect ear mites early.

When your cat decides to get comfortable and curls up on your lap, you can hear a satisfying purr from deep in its throat. A cat often starts to knead with its front paws. Kneading is nothing more than the "milk-kneading" kittens use to stimulate the flow of mother's milk. We assume that this is an expression of well-being not unlike that felt by the kitten in the comfort of the nest.

Fear and Aggression

When frightened or distressed, cats are quick to become aggressive. Outright, pure aggression is extremely rare. When afraid, a cat's whole body becomes tense and seems to shrink, possibly because the head pulls back towards the body. The cat usually extends its front legs, exposing the claws. If the situation worsens, the cat moves its legs closer to the body, a position that allows it to strike quickly and effectively, if necessary. The hair on the back of the neck and body stands up, which does not occur at any other time. The tail is rigid, the tip whipping back and forth—clearly a sign that the animal is excited. The ears pull back, slightly to the side. When the whiskers are flat against the head, the cat is showing fear. When they are spread forward, fanlike, the cat is showing aggression. The pupils of a frightened cat are wide open, but when a cat becomes aggressive, they are as small as the head of a pin. This is a certain signal that an attack is imminent. A cat's wild hissing is a warning meant to frighten whatever is confronting it. Even more effective is the "spitting" sound that occurs without the presence of saliva. This spitting sound is more like a short hiss that starts with a "kh." If a cat is terrified, it will emit loud, high, almost hysterical screams or a heart-breaking howl with whining. When aggression outweighs fear, a cat lets out a growl that comes from deep inside the throat. Even if you know nothing about cats, this serves as an unmistakable warning.

Feeling Bad

A cat resting with its front paws folded under often does not feel quite right. Even though the head extends, the whole body looks shorter. The tail is close to the body and motionless. The fur looks dull and not well groomed. The cat looks somehow like a bird with puffed-up feathers. The ears are usually turned slightly sideways and back; the eyes are half closed and staring into an empty distance. Sometimes a cat will even be purring quietly, perhaps as a cautious message to other cats or as a comfort for itself. If you try to make contact, more often than not, the cat will try to get away from you.

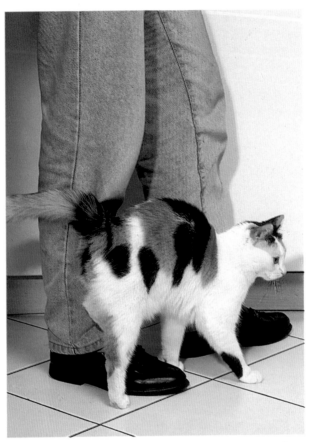

Above: If a cat is rubbing its body against your legs as it walks around you, the cat is marking you with its scent and may also want you to pet it or feed it.

Right: If your cat becomes aggressive, it means that it is frightened. The position of its ears is the best indicator of what a cat is about to do.

Cats with Access to the Outdoors

When a cat has access to the outside, it can exercise its species-specific social behavior, and it can hunt.

Indoor cats develop a considerable deficit in the way they handle social contact. No matter how much contact a cat has with its owner, a human can never take the place of contact and interaction with other cats.

Social Behavior and the Hunting Instinct

When it comes to other members of their species, cats have their likes and dislikes. They may develop a close friendship with some cats, while others are their archenemies. The social structure of an area's cat population is highly complicated, and a cat must integrate itself into this structure with as little fuss as possible.

Invitation to Play

A cat that is ready to play usually approaches you with its tail straight up in the air. Because it is concentrating on you, its ears pointed slightly forward. The pupils are small; the whiskers are spread wide, pointing forward. When some cats are excited, they signal that play can begin by kneading with their front paws.

At the same time, cats often produce a short, encouraging meow or a very peculiar purr, not unlike the one a mother cat would make when she is telling her kittens that it is time to play.

If something catches a cat's attention, its eyes open wide, its whiskers fan out as far as they can go, and its ears point forward. When all of these indications are present, something has your cat's total attention.

Symptoms of Illnesses

If your cat seems to be under the weather, check for specific symptoms. Check the litter box for signs of diarrhea or vomiting. Observe your cat to see if the situation is getting worse. If that is the case, check its temperature (see "Nursing Care: Caring For an Ill Cat," pages 83 to 84) and, if necessary, make an appointment with your practitioner or veterinarian (see "The Most Frequently Occurring Illnesses," page 55). In most instances, these ailments quickly pass. If the problem seems to be temporary or if you want to supplement professional treatment, you might want to use one of the remedies listed in "Natural Remedies in Your Medicine Cabinet," pages 16 to 17.

You can observe a cat's territorial behavior inside a house or apartment. Most adult cats have lost little of their innate territorial behavior, even if you have neutered them. They guard, mark, control, conquer, and defend their space. Given the chance, they spend many hours each day tending to it.

On the other hand, the hunting instinct is not as uniformly developed in every cat. In addition to the obvious differences between breeds, the example set by a cat's mother plays a vital role. A mother that is an experienced and eager hunter will teach her offspring to be good hunters, while Persian cats, generally speaking, have had little or no contact with the outside world for centuries and know very little about hunting or what to do with a mouse.

Behavioral

Sometimes cats develop behavioral problems that the owner finds highly irritating. Without exception, the cause is poor handling of the animal or constant stress. The cat is never being intentionally malicious or menacing. Rather, the problem is a sign that the cat is suffering badly and is trying to get your attention. It is telling you this through inappropriate behavior. If your cat cannot adjust to a new situation in a reasonable amount of time and if you cannot change the situation, you need to find a new home for the cat.

Failure to Remain Housebroken

The most common behavioral problem in cats occurs when they suddenly won't use the litter box. This is particularly true for unneutered adult females that are unable to solve internal conflicts. Almost deliberately, they urinate, sometimes right in front of the owner, on a bed or a carpet. A conflict situation often arises because they have become sexually mature or they are missing the company of other cats. However, other things can cause the same problem, including moving to a new house, the arrival of a new family member, and changes in their environment such as using new cat litter or changing the location of the litter box.

Discovering the cause of the problem and removing it will often solve the problem. While you are searching for the problem, you may find that a Bach flower remedy is helpful. However, you or your practitioner must design the remedy for your cat and for the particular situation. If for some reason you cannot change or remove the reason for the behavior, such as a move or the birth of a new baby, Bach flower remedies will still be helpful.

Destructive Behavior

Cats very seldom become so aggressive that they attack furniture or other objects and seriously damage them. Such behavior is usually a sign of boredom caused by loneliness. The introduction of another cat as a playmate or the freedom to go outside often works wonders.

Incessant Licking

This behavior occurs fairly frequently in adult cats. Instead of normal grooming some cats will lick and scratch incessantly until they have removed all the fur, and only bare skin remains in a specific area. The sides, the belly, between the toes, and behind the knees and the thighs are favorite spots for excessive licking. The result is usually a skin rash. But before you look for psychological reasons, make sure you rule out allergies, kidney problems, and infectious diseases. In addition, a heavy parasite

Problems

infestation can drive a cat into such a state that it can only deal with the problem by scratching furiously. In the absence of a physical illness, psychological conflict is usually the reason for bare and inflamed skin. Since the cat is unable to deal with the situation, incessant licking acts as a diversion. Further, this behavior may become compulsive. The underlying reason could be loneliness, boredom, or jealousy, a family move to another house, or any number of other drastic changes in the cat's environment.

Therefore, treating the skin inflammation will only be effective if you can remove the cause for the unhealthy behavior. An individually designed Bach flower remedy can be very useful in helping the cat regain its normal grooming habits.

Scratching and Biting

Most cats inadvertently strike out at a human hand, particularly when they are young. When a cat starts to bite or scratch, pulling away is not always the best way to handle the situation because that may serve as an invitation to the cat to increase its hold on your hand. However, if you move your hand towards the animal, the cat will almost always let go all by itself.

You can break a young cat of this habit by removing it from your lap and putting it on the floor as soon as you detect signs of aggression, such as the tail whipping back and forth. Bach flower remedies can also be very helpful.

Cats may strike out suddenly while you are patting them because they have had negative experiences with other people. A cat who has had bad experiences with other people is constantly torn between enjoyment and fear while you pet it. As soon as fear outweighs enjoyment, it will strike out. In such cases, only a lot of patience and a great deal of positive interaction will make a difference. Here, too, Bach flower remedies can help.

Sucking and Kneading

Cats that knead on a soft surface are expressing a sense of complete well-being. This kneading is just like the so-called milking step that a kitten uses to stimulate the milk flow of its nursing mother. If a cat that has been weaned shows such behavior by licking and kneading all kinds of objects, for example, a sweater, your hair, stuffed animals, or couch pillows, you can safely assume that the owner took it from its mother too early, not allowing it to satisfy its sucking needs. Cats from large litters also show this behavior if they were not able to nurse as much as they wanted.

We recommend treatment with a Bach flower remedy. If this fails to bring results, you might have to put up with the behavior. In most cases, the cat will change on its own when it gets older. If the habit is a real nuisance, give the cat an object, such as a stuffed animal, and restrict the kneading and licking to that object.

Cats always keep an eye on their surroundings and love to know what is going on in their neighborhood. That's the reason they often choose elevated places to sit.

Introducing Your Cat to the Outdoors

• A kitten should be at least five months old before you introduce it to the outdoors; later is even better.

• In the beginning, take your cat outside and stay with it. Every time you go back inside, give the cat a little treat. You want to combine the idea of coming home and being rewarded with something tasty, and then you want to indelibly imprint this on the cat's mind. You may want to plan your kitten's first outing alone so that it takes place just prior to its regular feeding time. That would limit the amount of time your kitten will want to stay outside. But whatever you do, make sure your cat has an identification tag on its collar before it goes out by itself for the first time.

• Make a distinctive noise, such as shaking the dry-food box, opening a can, or whistling, each time you feed your cat. Once the animal has learned to associate this noise with food, it will come running home the minute it hears the signal.

• If you don't want to open the door every time the cat wants to come inside,

What to Do
When Your Cat Is Missing

TIP

Have an identifying code or number tattooed inside your cat's ear.

On occasion, a cat that has access to the outside does not come home one day. Perhaps it simply can't find its way back. It might have found a place with food that it likes better then what it receives at home. Maybe a door closed unexpectedly, trapping it in a cellar or shed in the neighborhood. On the other hand, someone might have stolen your cat, or a car might have hit it. Sometimes animals that have not been neutered follow their mating instincts and are too busy to remember to come home.

If your cat is generally reliable and always comes home at a certain time, don't wait too long to take action. In addition to looking for it yourself, post flyers around the neighborhood and ask the owners of small businesses if you can post announcements in their store. Your poster should suggest that the cat might be trapped in a cellar or shed in the neighborhood. In addition, notify the animal shelters in your area. No later than three to four days after your cat is missing, call the veterinarians in your area and ask

them if they have treated a cat resembling yours. You may also want to call the police.

After a week, expand your efforts by putting an announcement or advertisement in your local newspaper. Your cat might have jumped unnoticed into an open car. Moving vans are especially attractive "caverns" that entice cats to do some exploring. People may have thought the animal was a stray until they found an identifying tattoo. Then, they may have set the animal free too far away from your home for it to find its way back to you.

Never give up hope! People have found their cats months and even years after they have lost them because of the cat's identification. By the way, if a strange cat that doesn't have an identification tag tries to make a new home in your house or on your property, consider first that it might be comeone else's cat and notify the police or the animal shelters in your area.

When two cats meet, they first sniff each other to see if they know each other. If they have met before, they usually touch noses briefly as a polite greeting. If they don't know each other, the sniffing intensifies and includes "checking" the hind quarters, followed by hissing. The weaker of the two cats usually "turns tail" at that point.

consider installing a cat door. This works well for everyone involved. Cats are quick learners; simply hold the flap open and let your cat go through it.

In the beginning, you might have to hold the door open when the cat uses it. However, if you place a little treat on the other side of the door, you will be surprised how quickly your cat gets the hang of opening the door without your help.

The Indoor Cat

If you plan to keep your cat indoors all the time, consider getting more than one cat. If you get two at the same time, be sure you provide sufficient stimuli and space for physical activities. Cats that have been indoors from the time of their birth will never miss the outdoors. But a cat that has had access to the outside will have a difficult time getting used to a life restricted to the indoors.

The overwhelming majority of cats are very social animals and, particularly in the early period of their lives, are not very good at occupying themselves when alone. For this reason, having two cats is always better than having one, especially if you have to leave the house to go to work.

Gender is not an important issue when you introduce cats prior to puberty; very seldom will you encounter problems. When it comes to adult cats, though, female cats adjust less well to each other than do male cats. Regardless of gender, make sure that the cats are similar in age. Older, more sedentary cats feel put upon if they have to contend with an enthusiastic youngster. On the other hand, younger cats have no real companionship if they have to share their home with an older cat.

Indoor cats need a few special arrangements. In addition to the obvious and basic things, such as a place for sleeping, eating, and a litter box, cats need places to climb and to hide and places from which they can look outside. The more of these, the better. Provide a place for your cat to sharpen its claws. The best way to do that is to buy or build a scratching pad or post. This is good for the cat and for your furniture. Also, make sure that the cat has enough toys: a piece of fur, a box to hide in, and a squeaky toy. All of these will keep your cat fit and happy.

Make sure your house is "cat safe." Time and again, cats have burned their paws on a hot stove. You can easily prevent such accidents by simply placing a pot over the heating elements while they are still hot. An open tilting window is another accident waiting to happen. Many a cat has lost its life because of this kind of window. The animal tries to squeeze through and gets stuck between the window and the frame, sliding into the opening that gets narrower and narrower. The more frantic its attempts to free itself the farther down it slides until, in the end, it finally strangles itself or seriously injures its internal organs.

You must install screens on all windows and balconies. A fall from a win-

Hunting Instinct

Some indoor cats do play havoc with the furniture in your house. Don't scold them because they are only following their hunting instincts. Somewhere inside even the most serene cat lives a wild tiger. However, regular playing time and proper toys can channel these hunting instincts into activities that won't damage your furniture.

Cats kept strictly indoors like to hunt insects, but they don't know that some of them, such as wasps and bees, might be dangerous. If a bee or wasp stings your cat, use Bach Flower Rescue Remedy and cold arnica compresses on the injury. These stings usually take place on the paws (see "Natural Remedies in Your Medicine Cabinet," pages 16 to 17). Since cats with stings are in great pain, quickly take them to the veterinarian or practitioner for treatment.

Opposite page: Cats that are kept indoors exclusively need many different objects and toys that allow them plenty of opportunities for stimulating play.

Below left: Indoor cats need an opportunity for scratching. A scratching post that also allows for climbing is best.

Below right: It is a widely held belief that cats are by nature solitary; nothing could be further from the truth. Indoor cats, in particular, love to have a partner in play.

Above: If you don't want your cat to stray from your property, you need to make the yard "cat proof," which isn't that easy. Cats are excellent climbers and jumpers, and some have an amazing determination when it comes to digging holes under fences. In any case, curbing their instinctive urge to be free and to roam is difficult. You might find that it is simpler to install a screen on a porch or balcony.

Below: All cats eat grass on a more or less regular basis. Grass aids in digestion and is helpful in getting rid of fur balls. If your cat is an indoor cat, you need to provide some green plants, These are essential for the cat's health.

dow or balcony can cause severe, often fatal, injuries. If you are renting, and the landlord won't give you permission to install screens, don't let your cat out on the balcony unless it is in a harness and leash, and even then, only when you can watch it. Tying the leash directly around the cat's neck is dangerous because the cat might strangle itself. House plants can also be a source of danger. Quite a few ornamental plants are highly poisonous (see "Dangers," page 27). Even a small piece of such a plant can cause severe poisoning. Although yucca plants, rubber tree plants, and succulents, such as cacti, are poisonous, they are safe to have around the house because cats don't like them. Nonpoisonous plants that cats do like include lilies, cypress grass, and all bamboo plants.

But even in a house that has everything it needs, a cat still has to have contact with its human housemates. Never deprive a cat of daily physical contact. If you have to leave the house in the morning to go to work, your cat will

Nutrition

Most cats do perfectly well on commercial, canned food if you also give them something solid to chew on, such as meat cartilage, once a week. This keeps their gums healthy (see "Tartar," page 58).

Sometimes, however, cats chew on objects that may splinter, such as twigs or chicken bones. These then become trapped between the teeth or cause injuries inside the mouth. If your cat acts strangely, for example, turning its head and trying to reach inside its mouth with a paw, and you notice an increase in the flow of saliva, it has probably had such a chewing accident. If you are unable to remove the foreign object yourself, ask for professional help. Splinters can cause serious injuries in the mouth cavity and the throat, as well as cause internal injuries. (For more about transporting sick animals, see "Caring For an Ill Cat," pages 90 to 92. For information on treating these injuries, as well as injured gums, see "Foreign Objects in the Mouth Cavity," page 57.)

always greet you enthusiastically when you come home at night. This is the best time for close interaction.

Cats and Other House Pets

If other pets live in the house with a cat, be sure you know what the needs and the species-specific behaviors of each are.

Many people believe that cats and dogs are archenemies. Actually, however, this is not always the case. From a cat's point of view, everything depends on the kind of experiences the cat has had with dogs, particularly while it was still a kitten. That is what will determine whether the cat will be friendly towards a dog or be afraid and react with aggressive hissing.

Painful misunderstandings between a cat and a dog frequently occur. A cat's tail that is whipping back and forth is in a defensive mode and tells us that the cat is ready to strike. For a dog, on the other hand, a wagging tail is a friendly greeting; consequently, that is how a dog reacts to the motion of a cat's tail. A dog is going to be very disappointed when, instead of the friendly rub it expects, it gets hit on the nose with the cat's claws. Of course, we also know of dogs that simply don't like cats—a feeling cats can usually sense. Most cats are smart enough to simply take off rather than get into a tiff with an unfriendly dog.

The ideal situation occurs when cats and dogs grow up together. In such cases, they often become close friends. Although an adult dog usually has no problem getting used to a kitten, a cat finds it more difficult to get used to a puppy (see "The Older Cat," page 64).

With most birds, cats are natural predators. That's why uncaged birds are in danger and need protection. With some birds, such as parrots, however, it is the other way around: they can severely injure a cat with their sharp claws. The ideal "entertainment" for a cat is an aquarium. But make sure that you can close the top of the aquarium securely, because deep inside every cat is the heart of a fisherman. A cat will also consider small animals, such as hamsters, as prey. On the other hand, a cat can become

TIP

You should check all toys, particularly stuffed toys, for plastic eyes, ears, or noses that might come loose and that your cat might swallow. If these items lodge in the intestinal tract, they can cause severe illnesses.

53

Above: If you have other animals in the house besides your cat, be careful! Always remember that hamsters, fish, and birds can be potential prey.

Below: Many harmonious and close friendships exist between cats and dogs, especially when they grow up together.

TIP

When a cat and a dog meet for the first time, make sure that the cat is sitting on higher ground and, if necessary, has the opportunity to escape to a book shelf or other safe place.

good friends with animals that are a bit bigger, guinea pigs, for example. The same holds true for miniature rabbits. When providing for the happiness of your cat, never forget that its ancestors were wild predators. When a cat is acting out its innate drives, it can harm or even kill other animals. Keep that in mind if you are planning to introduce other animals into the house.

The Most Frequently Occurring Illnesses

Recognizable Symptoms	Possible Causes	What You Can Do	You Should See Your Veterinarian
Sleeps a great deal; stops playing; is apathetic	Beginning of or chronic infectious disease; cat may be bored	Take temperature; observe closely; use remedies that strengthen the body's defense mechanism, such as *Echinacea*	If body temperature is above 103°F (39.5°C) or below 100.5°F (38°C); if no improvement within three days
Eats little or not at all; chews on one side only; races to the food dish but does not eat; inflamed throat and gums	Toothache, gum infection; sore throat; in rare cases, liver disease	Give remedies stimulating the defense mechanism; treat inflamed gums with chamomile tea; in case of sore throat use neck compress; take temperature	In case of toothache; infection; if no changes in mouth or no improvement within three days; if temperature is above 103°F (39.5°C) or below 100.5°F (38°C)
Vomiting, possibly accompanied by gastritis; blocked intestines (constant vomiting and no bowl movement)	Upset stomach; poisoning; fever	Withhold food for twenty-four hours, use a light diet for three to four days; instead of water, give diluted peppermint tea; give one tablet of *Nux vomica* 6×	If body temperature is above 103°F (39.5°C) or below 100.5°F (38°C); in case of peppermint tea; every constant vomiting and obvious weakness; if vomiting blood; check temperature if no improvement within three days
Vomiting, possibly accompanied by fever	Spoiled food; poisoning; infection	Withhold food for twenty-four hours, for three to four days; instead of water give diluted chamomile tea; use charcoal in Kaopectate, one tablespoon (15ml), several times a day; essential to take temperature	If body temperature is above 103°F (39.5°C) or below 100.5°F (38°C); then use a light diet in case of frequent and watery or bloody diarrhea; in case of obvious weakness; if no improvement within three days
Limping	Sprain or contusion; fractures or injured ligaments; beginning of an abscess; insect bite	Cold (arnica) compresses, using one tablet Arnica 4×; check legs for wounds or crusts of dried blood	If leg seems dislocated; if unable to move; if shys away from being touched; serious wounds
Boils or hardening under the skin	Abscess; tumor	Compresses with healing earth; give *Hepar sulfuris* 8× or *Myristica sebifera* 6× to bring abscess to a head; to heal: give one tablet of Traumeel several times a day	In any case to obtain a proper diagnosis: abscess or tumor
Frequently shakes head and scratches ears; black deposits inside the ears	Ear mites	Apply oxygen-enriched olive oil or calendula oil to the inside of the ear, massage the base of the ear; clean ears carefully	If no obvious explanation for the behavior; if itching and deposits are still present after ten days
Frequent licking and scratching all over the body	Parasites; behavioral problems; hormone imbalances; less likely: kidney or metabolic diseases	Check for parasites, comb fur with a flea comb; use flea powder; add garlic and vitamin B (brewer's yeast) to food	If no parasites are present

Case Histories from My Practice

If a poisonous substance, such as paint or motor oil, covers a cat's fur, a neck collar is a practical device that prevents the cat from ingesting any of the poison as it tries to lick itself clean. This method is also very helpful when you want to prevent your cat from licking a wound.

Poisoning

Cats are frequently exposed to poisonous chemicals. Often they are harmed and sometimes even killed by these, which are everywhere. Occasionally, cats fall victim to people's stupidity or malice.

This is what had happened to Joscha, a female cat who was a year and a half old. The cat had come back from one of her outings with her fur a total mess. The owner called me, greatly concerned. She thought somebody, perhaps as a joke, had poured oil paint or used motor oil all over her cat. Even though the fur had kept much of the poisonous liquid off of her skin, the poison had entered her system when she had tried to clean herself. Joscha was already weak, refusing to eat or drink

While still on the phone I suggested that the owner administer some Bach Flower Rescue Remedy and give the cat a bath with a neutral soap. I immediately got in my car to visit the distressed cat. When I arrived, the owner had just finished with the bath and was drying the fur. Joscha was lethargic and showed no sign of protest during the examination. Her pupils were large, and she was producing a lot of saliva. Her body temperature was 100.5°F (38°C). I immediately started to administer extra liquids intravenously in order to help her kidneys clear the system of toxins and to support the circulatory system. I also gave her a large dose of a vitamin B-complex to help regenerate the nervous system and to stimulate liver function. In order to prevent possible permanent damage to the liver, I also prescribed *Mariendistel* (milk thistle) extract in tablet form. I asked the owner to give the cat a preparation consisting of charcoal, Kaolin, and pectin several times a day. This is helpful in neutralizing the poison in the stomach and intestinal tract. Finally, to prevent the cat from licking her fur, we attached a color around her neck.

I returned to Joscha's house the same evening and again the following day. The owner was to continue all medications as prescribed, including the intravenous injectons. We also decided to bathe her twice more, trying to get as much of the toxic substances as possible out of her fur.

By the third day, Joscha had improved considerably. Since there seemed to be

no damage to her central nervous system, which would have resulted in irreversible damage, we knew that her chances for survival were good. And indeed, after four days, she began to eat. One week later, she had completely recovered.

However, four weeks later, the results of a blood test showed that her liver was not functioning normally. Therefore, we continued the treatment with the *Mariendistel* (milk thistle) extract and the vitamin B-complex. Six weeks later, when a checkup showed no further symptoms, we discontinued all medication.

Foreign Object in the Mouth Cavity

Cats love to chew on bones. This is a typical habit for a predatory animal. Sometimes a bone will splinter and injure the inside of the mouth. The splinter might get stuck between the teeth, in the gums, or between the jaws. If the owner

A dinner table is a great temptation for any cat. But what might be a culinary delight for people might not be good for cats. Sometimes, it can even be fatal. Such is the case with chicken bones, which splinter very easily. Splintered bones can cause injury inside the mouth and in the intestines. You can chase a cat away from the table with a little squirt of lemon juice or by holding an onion under its nose. But be prepared: a cat will always try to get up on the dinner table.

Healthy gums are pink and smooth. The best way to prevent problems is to give a cat a few pieces of cartilage once a week. Chewing the cartilage helps prevent tartar from accumulating on the teeth.

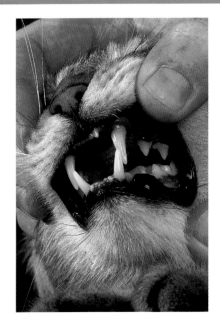

a chicken bone had jammed between opposing molars, across his upper jaw. The splinter had penetrated the gum on one side, which must have caused a lot of pain. I had to use a dental instrument to dislodge the bone. As soon as I removed this torturous object, Mike regained his composure. He allowed me to apply an herbal extract to his gums without putting up much of a fight. In order to support the healing process, I prescribed arnica tablets in homeopathic strength.

When I saw Mike three days later, all signs of the injury had disappeared, and his gums were absolutely normal.

doesn't promptly attend to such accidents, the cat can suffer a serious inflammation and even an infection in the mouth cavity. The owner will quickly realize that something is wrong: not only does the cat salivate a lot, it will also be very upset if it has a foreign object stuck in its mouth. The cat will shake its head back and forth, sometimes walking backwards, continuously reaching into its mouth with a paw. This is exactly what Mike, a five-year-old male cat had been doing.

Mike's owner came to my office anxious and very worried. Deep growling sounds came from the cat carrier box. Mike was so agitated that we had to use force to get him out of the box. He was fighting so hard that we had to wrap him in a blanket and hold him down in order for me to examine him. As soon as I looked into his mouth, I knew why the animal was behaving this way: a piece of

Tartar

A common problem for domesticated cats is tartar buildup along the gum line. Sadly enough, owners usually recognize this rather late. When they don't remove the tartar it can cause inflammation, infections, abscesses of the gums, and even loss of teeth.

The owner of a six-year-old cat, Felix, came to my office because she had noticed that her cat had very bad breath and that his appetite was very erratic. The owner also brought Mona, her female cat, for her annual examination. I only needed one look at Felix's mouth: he had never had his teeth cleaned, and the tartar buildup was so heavy that it had formed a thick layer over his entire back teeth. The tissue surrounding the plaque was inflamed and swollen, and one of his molars was loose. Such severe accumulation is impossible to treat without anesthesia. We proceeded to make an ap-

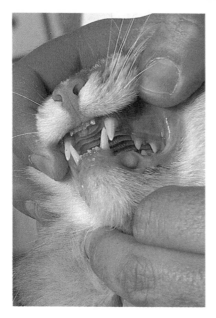

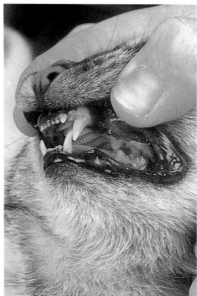

Left: The cause of inflamed, swollen gums above the teeth may be poor nutrition or tartar buildup. In addition, infectious diseases or a weak constitution can also cause inflamed gums and affect the health of the teeth.

Right: If you don't have tartar removed on a regular basis, it will form thick deposits on the labial surface of the teeth, resulting in gum infections. Avoid giving your cat commercial food containing sugar, which encourages the buildup of tartar. Solid dry food, on the other hand, helps prevent tartar buildup.

pointment with a veterinarian who would do the necessary treatment on the operating table.

Mona's situation was not nearly as bad. She did have some tartar buildup on her molars, but her gums were only slightly inflamed. Mona was a patient and quiet cat, and I had no problem cleaning her teeth. After I removed the tartar, I applied an herbal tincture to the gums. I gave both cats a prescription for an herbal extract to mobilize their immune systems. In addition, I advised the owner that the main reason for tartar accumulation is the sugar content in pet food. Glucose syrup or caramel, often listed in the ingredients, is nothing more than sugar! The damaging effects of the sugar are intensified by the bits of dry food that remain in the mouth, sometimes hours after a cat has eaten. For that reason, I highly recommend that you feed your cats home-cooked food every

now and then. Let them chew on veal cartilage or a beef bone, both of which act as cleansers. You can enhance this self-cleaning procedure by giving your cat a piece of raw meat the size of a mouse. Cats usually delight in chewing on raw meat.

Felix and Mona came to my office one week later for a checkup. Even though Felix had lost one molar, his gums were healthy and pink, and his bad breath had totally disappeared. He voiced no objection when I treated his gums one more time with the herbal extract. Mona's teeth and gums were picture perfect. The owner reported that her cats were delighted with the new regimen of a piece of meat once a week. They often chewed on the meat for half an hour. We decided that Felix should come to my office every six months to have his teeth checked, while Mona only needed to be checked once a year.

Sometimes two mother cats share in the raising of their young. Many mothers are even willing to take on strange kittens, raising both their own and the stranger's. How fortunate for those kittens whose own mother has become sick!

Nipple Infections

Nipple infection is a common problem within the first few weeks after a cat has given birth. If the owner doesn't detect the problem in time, it can have fatal consequences for the new kittens. For farm cats, who generally give birth in hidden places, such an infection usually results in the death of the whole litter. However, if the owner detects the infection in its early stages, treatment is not difficult, and the owner only needs to provide some supplemental feedings for a few days until the mother cat is again able to produce sufficient amounts of milk for the kittens.

One beautiful day in the spring, a very concerned cat owner called my office asking me to come to her house as quickly as possible. A pregnant cat had appeared at her door three days before and had given birth to a litter of four kittens. During the last few days, she had noticed that the kittens were very agitated and that the mother cat had stopped eating.

When I arrived, I checked the mother cat first. Her temperature was 103°F (39.5°C). Her breast felt hot to the touch, and parts of it were obviously congested and hard. I examined the nipples, and when I carefully squeezed them, they produced only a few drops of milk. The examination was obviously painful for the cat. A nipple infection in its most classical form!

The first order of business was to feed the kittens with a commercial kitten formula. Next, I gave the mother an injection of an herbal immune-supporting preparation, as well as a remedy often used with great success in such cases: a homeopathic remedy in tablet form which the owner was to administer every two hours. In addition, I advised the owner to apply cold, wet compresses to the inflamed breast several times a day.

The owner called the next day and reported that the mother cat's condition had improved considerably. Her appetite had returned to normal, and she was taking care of her kittens again. We decided to continue the supplemental feedings for the kitten for three more days, until the nipples were soft and the milk production had returned to normal.

Chronic Ear Infections

Ear mites are parasites with remarkable staying power, and they are often the cause of ear infections. Owners must consistently use the prescribed medications in order to avoid a relapse of the ear infection. Most medications used to treat ear mites contain very toxic substances, such as DDT.

Penny, a four-year-old cat, had needed medication to treat ear mites several times during her life. But because of its toxicity, the owner could only use the medication for a short time, and, consequently, the infection continued to recur. No doubt, the fact that Penny was an outdoor cat played a role in the frequent

appearance of the parasites. This time, the infestation was particularly severe, and Penny had deep scratch wounds in and around the ears.

The examination revealed the inside of both ears covered with a thick crust, created by substances from the ear mites, and with partially infected wounds. The base of the ear on one side was already painful to the touch. Before I started cleaning the ears, I softened the crusty deposits with calendula oil. I then rinsed out the ears, again using calendula.

I then applied a calendula salve, massaging the base of both ears in order to get as much of the oil as possible into the inner ear. I treated the inflamed scratching wounds with arnica salve, *Echinacea*, and calendula. Penny's owner was to put calendula oil in both ears twice a day and to add a homeopathic remedy to her food.

Penny came for a checkup four days later. The scratches were beginning to heal, and the black deposits were smaller but not yet totally eliminated. Since Penny seemed annoyed about having the oil put in her ears and, as a result, strayed even more often from the house, I sug-

When putting liquid medication in the ear canal, hold the head, as shown, and gently fold the ear back. Never insert the dropper into the ear canal, because this could cause severe injury.

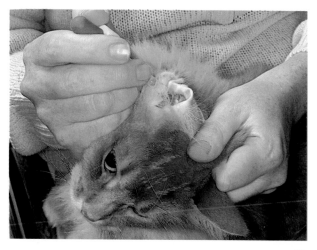

The confrontation between these two cats is playful, harmless, and typical of the action between cats. However, sexually mature male cats often get into very serious fights with rivals. While their fur provides good protection against some injuries, deep scratches or bites often become infected.

gested that we interrupt the treatment for the next two days. I decided that we would start again, but that this time we would use oxygenated olive oil, which only needs to be applied every other day. The treatment would take a little longer, but the cat would be better able to deal with the procedure. Penny and her owner went home after I cleaned out both ears with oxygenated olive oil.

Another checkup two weeks later showed no signs of inflammation or any presence of ear mites.

Abscess after a Fight

An abscess is an accumulation of puss under the skin. It is usually the result of an injury that is relatively small on the surface but very deep, such as a biting wound. Although the injury heals superficially, the tissue underneath, deprived of air, becomes infected. The secretions of the would have no place to drain, and turn into puss. When the pressure inside the tissue becomes too great, the abscess breaks open, emptying the puss, totally or partially.

Sexually mature male cats often get into fights with other male cats. Frequently, both cats sustain deep scratches and bites. After Carlo, a male Siamese cat, was in such a fight, his owner brought him to my office. Carlo was only ten months old, but he was already a real Don Juan, constantly on the prowl. However, his latest outing had lasted three days. When he finally came home, he was truly a pitiful sight.

During my examination, I found several injuries. One of his ears had a deep

Pancreatic Problems

Most of the enzymes produced by the pancreas and used by the digestive system empty into the small intestine as needed. An acute viral infection, or a chronic one, can seriously impair the function of this important gland. Only rarely does the pancreas begin to dysfunction slowly and without apparent cause. This problem is rather unpredictable, and its effects are different for different animals. Some of the symptoms are: a ravenous appetite while continuing to lose weight, frequent bouts of diarrhea, and severe flatulence. A definite diagnosis, however, depends on stool and blood tests.

Sometimes, the cat's food needs to be supplemented with an enzyme preparation, perhaps for life. While this will mean additional financial and time commitments on the part of the owner, the cat will live a normal life.

tear, and a thick crust covered the top of his nose. But it was the left side of his face that was most severely injured. The eye was very swollen, and crust covered the fur from the ear down to the lower jaw. After I cleaned his face, I discovered a large abscess underneath the skin on the cheek. When I removed the surface crust, an enormous amount of puss and wound secretion rushed out through a small hole. I rinsed the opening of the abscess with a preparation that disinfects and stimulates healing. We also gave him an injection of an *Echinacea* preparation and *Myristica sebifera* 4×. In addition, we treated him for ten minutes in a rather strong magnetic field. I recommended that the owner make sure that the facial wounds remained open to avoid another blockage of the wound secretions. We continued this regimen for the next three days and also gave Carlo Traumeel tablets for the next ten days.

Three weeks later, Carlo was his old self again, except for the scar on his ear. I suggested that the owner might want to have Carlo neutered; he would roam less, become more of a house cat, and have fewer fights with other male cats. His owner had Carlos neutered four weeks later.

The Old Age
of a Cat

By the time they are seven or eight years old, cats will develop the first, almost unnoticeable, signs of aging. The life expectancy of each cat depends to a great degree on how and where the cat lives. Statistics show that outdoor cats live about eight to ten years and indoor cats about twelve to fifteen years. But even twenty-year-old cats are not all that uncommon. Among purebred cats, Siamese cats live the longest. However, purebred cats generally have a shorter life span than mixed breeds. The reason might be the intense inbreeding of the former.

Male cats, regardless of whether they are indoor or outdoor cats, have a greater life expectancy if you have them neutered.

Physical Development

At first glance, older cats don't look all that much different from younger cats. Sometimes you might notice a drooping

TIP

Pureeing the food makes digestion easier for a cat that is missing several teeth.

When a Siamese, such as this, is a very young kitten, her coat starts out white and she has the same natural curiosity as any other kitten. As she develops, the dark points begin to show and she displays a demeanor of elegance. Among breeds the Siamese, along with the related Burmese, live a particularly long time.

belly, a swayback, or in very old cats, ragged, shaggy fur. The whole posture of an older cat seems stunted, and its sides sink in. The fur between and on the ears begins to thin, and, particularly in black cats, the individual hairs around the mouth and the sides turn white.

You can see the most obvious effects of aging on the teeth. Just as people do, cats start losing teeth, beginning with the incisors and eventually some of the molars. The remaining teeth seem to grow longer as the gums recede. Because of the increasing loss of calcium, the teeth take on a porcelainlike appearance.

Used in small amounts, foods containing high protein, as well as small amounts of sodium and potassium, are very gentle on the heart and kidneys of an older cat. The owner should remove

foods like giblets or heart from the menu and replace them with chicken and fish. While most older cats begin to eat less, some continue to have a good appetite and may even gain weight. In these cases, the owner will have to reduce the caloric content of the food.

Older cats become less active, and their gaits become stiff. They have trouble bending and difficulties grooming hard-to-reach parts of their body. No wonder the fur of an older cat begins to look scraggly, no matter how often the owner might brush the cat's fur. In particular, jumping becomes more and more difficult. They will avoid obstacles rather than attack and conquer them, the way they did when they were younger. They use their favorite resting places on shelves or a chest of drawers less and less.

TIP

You can help an older cat overcome the difficulty of reaching the much desired high perching spots by providing an intermediate landing place. A simple armchair, desk, or open shelf of a bookcase may be all that is needed to allow your cat to get from here to there. In some cases, you may find it's best to offer an inclined ramp so that your aging cat can continue to enjoy a favorite vantage point.

Digestive Problems

Age-related changes influence metabolism, and reduced fluid intake and lack of activity often lead to constipation (young cats tend more towards diarrhea).

In such cases, a modified diet is very helpful. Look for appropriate recipes in "Diet," pages 88 to 89. Flax seeds, soaked in water and then mixed with one spoon of paraffin oil, help to stimulate digestion.

If your older cat does not drink enough, offer milk diluted in water or a salt-free broth. If your cat's bowels do not move for more than three days, seek professional advice. Left untreated, constipation can cause blockages, and the hardened stool sometimes has to be removed surgically.

Joint Problems

Severe pain often accompanies degenerative processes in the joints. This is as true for cats as for people. A cat in pain avoids moving and jumping, and the lack of activity can lead to digestive problems, such as constipation. We can lessen the pain with natural remedies, such as ophidian extract, leeches, and magnet therapy. You'll find a discussion of the natural tratment of degenerative diseases in "Case Histories from My Practice," page 79.

Failing to use the litter box, leaving stool or urine elsewhere, is usually a sign of psychological stress: a way for your cat to express that something is seriously wrong. Older cats are even more sensitive to stress, showing disturbed behavior more often than younger cats.

A very old cat might need your help just to get into her favorite chair.

With advanced age, cats will lose some of their keen senses of smell and touch. Sight and hearing also begin to diminish. As cats age, their ability to focus on fast-moving objects, such as mice, diminishes, and they experience fewer and fewer hunting successes.

Signals from the nervous system slow down, and the aging process affects the brain. The loss of gray cells is so large that, at the end of a cat's long life, its brain is twenty-five-percent smaller than it was in its best years. In other words, the whole organism slowly begins to run down. No wonder that an older cat sleeps much more than a younger cat. But the sleep is not as deep as it was when the cat was younger. The need for warmth increases considerably, and many an old cat begins to look for an extra warm spot in the sun or near a heating outlet for sleeping.

You should have an older cat examined twice a year by a veterinarian or practitioner. These professionals can prescribe a regimen that can be helpful in strengthening the body and the psyche of the cat. Such natural revitalizing programs have to be designed individually for each animal, depending on the animal's constitution, the type of complaints, and its psychological state. You'll find a sample of such a strengthening regimen discussed in "Case Histories from My Practice," pages 75 and 76.

Psychological Development

Advancing age manifests itself in more than just physical symptoms. It also affects mental flexibility. An older cat becomes less and less interested in adventurous activities. Cats that go outside do so less often and won't roam the neighborhood as they did in the past. They are more likely to stay in the backyard when they need fresh air or physical activity. On cold days, particularly when it is wet, many old cats hate to go outside. For that reason, older cats, especially ones who have spent most of their lives outdoors, should now have a litter box inside.

Cats that led quiet lives in their younger days are a lot less likely to cope with changes in their daily routine when they begin to age. For instance, when you have your house renovated or when you move furniture around, never disturb your cat's favorite place or even move it to a different location. Small things are often important to an older cat, in a way

Psychological Stress

Older cats are more likely to suffer from psychological stress than younger cats. Psychological and physical problems may appear especially in cases in which an older cat has lost the person who has cared for it throughout its life; the family had to move; or the cat is confronted with a new family member (a person or another animal). The most frequent physical reaction to stress is gastritis (inflammation of the stomach lining), the treatment of which is discussed on page 76.

For the well-being of your older cat, try to avoid any drastic changes. But if a change is unavoidable, giving your cat extra love and attention will make it easier to adapt to the new situation. Ask your health practitioner for a Bach flower remedy that will help your animal to cope. As the example discussed in "Adjustment Problems," on page 74, shows, extreme situations can be handled with a great deal of patience.

Older cats get very annoyed when their sleeping/resting routine is interfered with. Likewise, a new kitten brought into the house is not easily accepted. Any change in the household or the exuberant activity of a brand-new young cat may bring about aggressive behavior or physical problems in an older cat.

that might seem unimportant to you. Putting an old cat in a kennel or other unfamiliar place when you go on vacation can be a truly traumatic event for the animal. All of a sudden, everything is different, and most older cats find change very difficult. The situation would be much better if you could arrange for a trusted person to care for the cat in your home.

Adding another member to its human family is also a severe interruption in the life of an older cat. This is especially true when the newcomer is a baby who becomes the center of attention. Many older cats will view the new arrival as simply unacceptable. In fact, the baby may be the cause of many sudden psychological problems for the cat. Painfully jealous and totally bewildered by the new situation, your cat might even become aggressive towards children.

The arrival of a new cat can also upset an aging one. If, however, the newcomer is well behaved, the older cat might not express too many objections. On the

Left: Senior citizens who live a quiet and regular life are perfect companions for older cats. Older people understand much better than children what it means to live with little aches and pains.

Right: Older cats sleep more than younger ones. On the average, cats spend about two-thirds of their lives sleeping. You should not think that your cat is withdrawing from you. On the contrary, spending time petting and holding is even more important for an older cat than it is for a younger one. Withholding contact can lead to psychological difficulties.

other hand, if the newcomer is a young-ster, full of life and temperamental, the older cat will feel very much put upon. When two cats have lived together for a long time, and one of them dies, bringing home a new companion immediately is not a good idea. Sometimes, however, an older cat will truly mourn and look for its missing companion. In such a case, bringing another cat home right away is a good idea. The companion should be somewhat younger, and experience has shown that a cat of the opposite sex works best.

Most aging cats become much more attached to their "special" person, and they look for opportunities to be much closer than they have been in the past. Lucky the cat that can be part of TV-watching time and can find a warm lap to snuggle on.

Susceptibility to Illness

Even though they enjoyed good health during their active years, many adult cats develop organic illnesses. Thus, regular visits to the veterinarian or practitioner are necessary. Checking your cat's teeth is particularly important. Gaps between teeth, inflammation of the gums, and buildup of tartar may make eating diffi-cult. Frequently, they are also a sign of an existing kidney disease. And when the kidneys are malfunctioning, the body's regulation of minerals is thrown into dis-array, affecting the health of the teeth.

Liver function also begins to slow down. This fact is particularly important for a veterinarian to keep in mind when prescribing medicine or administering anesthesia.

Internal Organs

The bladder and the kidneys are the organs most often affected by the aging process. Fortunately, we can treat any such illness very successfully with natural remedies, if we recognize the illness early. If the disease has advanced, however, we might need to use more powerful methods, including surgery. Preventive measures include making sure that an older cat drinks plenty of liquids (one-half to one bowl daily). If the practitioner or veterinarian suspects a kidney or bladder problem, he tests the urine and blood to make a proper diagnosis.

You can find suggestions for a diet to use with kidney diseases in "Diet," pages 88 to 89.

Just like people, older cats can suffer from serious metabolic diseases, the best known and most frequently occurring one of which is diabetes. As is the case with people, you need to keep your cat on a strict diet and have the animal's blood sugar tested frequently. In more advanced stages of diabetes, the cat will have to be on medication. If you carry out the treatment faithfully, your cat can lead a long, normal life.

The one advantage an older cat has over its younger counterpart is that it is almost immune to feline catarrh and FPL (feline panleukopenia or "distemper"), the killer diseases of young cats. Other infectious diseases, such as colds or diarrhea, rarely are a problem for older cats.

However, older cats have a tendency to develop tumors that may be benign or malignant. Since tumors can develop rapidly, you should have your cat checked every five to six months.

TIP

If your older cat reacts negatively to the arrival or presence of a new baby and cannot seem to get used to it, consider setting aside one room (size is not important) that can be off limits for the child now and in the future. Also consider blocking a door or hallway with a child-proof gate to prevent the child from running after the cat.

In addition to the joints and limbs, the internal organs are likely to be affected by the aging process. In addition to therapeutic measures, you can help your cat by supplying it with an appropriate diet.

not leave it alone during the final moments—no matter how upsetting it might be to watch. If you and your veterinarian have decided that euthanasia is necessary because of an incurable and painful disease, the animal will only feel the prick of the needle. Afterwards, your cat will simply "fall asleep" forever.

If you decide to let your cat die without intervention, you can make the journey easier by using Bach flower remedies. And if you are depressed and emotionally upset because of the impending event, Bach Flower Rescue Remedy might help you, too. You can apply the drops directly to the lips and massage it into the skin of the forehead or behind the ears. These directions work for the cat, as well as for you.

With advancing age, a cat spends more and more time at its favorite resting and sleeping place. Obviously, quiet, warmth, and continued care are the basic requirements for an older cat. Make time for your pet, provide proper nutrition and regular checkups, and nothing will stand in the way of your cat's dignified old age.

The Last Good-Bye

The time will come when you must say a final good-bye to your faithful companion. Regardless of whether your cat dies simply from old age or you release it from a painful illness through euthanasia, it is best for you and your cat that you

For a fee, your cat's body can be cremated. Burying a cat in the backyard is not a problem in most places, provided that the grave is deep enough. If in doubt, check with your county office for information about local ordinances.

TIP

When you feel bumps or lumps as you pat or stroke your cat, call your veterinarian or practitioner for an appointment.

The Most Frequently Occurring Illnesses

Recognizable Symptoms	Possible Reasons	What You Can Do	You Should See Your Veterinarian
Eats little or stops eating; chews food only on one side of mouth; discolored or loose teeth; gums swollen or inflamed	Toothaches or gum infection; liver or kidney problems; rarely: sore throat	Take temperature; give medication to stimulate immune system, such as *Echinacea*; treat inflamed gums with chamomile tea	In case of toothaches, thick tartar deposits, or recurring gum inflammation; no signs of injury in the mouth cavity; no improvement within three days; temperature above 103°F (39.5°C) or below 100.5°F (38°C)
Vomiting	Gastritis; spoiled or poisoned food; infectious disease; liver or kidney problems; tumors in the digestive tract	Take temperature; let cat fast for twenty-four hours, give peppermint tea only; follow with a light diet for three to five days; give *Nux vomica* 6× four to five times daily	If temperature above 103°F (39.5°C) or below 100.5°F (38°C); vomiting continues without bowel movements; blood in vomit; symptoms recur; no improvement within two days
Diarrhea	Spoiled or poisoned food; infectious disease; liver problems; tumors in the digestive tract	Take temperature; let cat fast for twenty-four hours, give only chamomile tea; light diet for three to five days; give 1 tablespoon (15ml) Kaopectate four times daily; use body compress	If temperature above 103°F (39.5°C) or below 100.5°F (38°C); bloddy diarrhea and severe stomachache; symptoms recur; vomiting occurs; no improvement within two days
Limping; avoids jumping	Bruised, sprained limb; arthritis; bone fracture or ligament damage; insect bite on the paw	Use arnica compress in cases of sprains and bruises; give Traumeel tablets several times a day; check for wounds or crusted blood; for arthritis: infrared-light treatment or wet, cold compresses (check which works best)	If dislocated fractures; difficult or impossible to move; large wounds; no improvement within two days
Lumps or defined hard bumps on the body	Tumor; less likely: abscess	Use compress with healing earth for abscesses; to bring abscess to a head, give *Hepar sulfuris* 8× or *Myristica sebifera* 6×; give Traumeel tablets to support healing	Always to detect a tumor early
Frequently shaking head and scratching ears; black or brown deposits inside the ears; no reaction when called or to noise	Ear mites; age-related deafness	For ear mites: oxygenated olive or calendula oil; for age-related deafness, be especially considerate	If no improvement after seven days of treatment; deafness suspected
Incessantly scratching the body	Parasites; kidney and metabolic diseases; hormone imbalance; rarely: behavioral problems (sometimes licking habit)	For flea infestation: treat with flea powder and use flea comb; use drops to support skin function	In the absence of parasites
Slow but steady weight loss; drinks irregularly	Kidney disease; metabolic problems; chronic infectious disease	Do not treat without knowing the reason for the symptoms	In order to establish proper diagnosis

Case Histories from My Practice

Traumatic events can cause severe reactions. Frightened and confused, the cat hides in a remote corner.

Adjustment Problems

Older cats that lose their familiar surroundings or the most important human being in their life can suffer from real depression. Often they simply hide somewhere, refusing contact with any other person. Psychological stress affects them more now than when they were younger. Preexisting illnesses might suddenly become worse or new illnesses, such as stress gastritis, might suddenly appear.

A woman who asked me to make a house call was aware of such a connection. She had adopted her two twelve-year-old cats from an animal shelter. The former owner had suddenly gone into a nursing home, and none of the owner's relatives was able to care for the two cats, Mimi and Momo.

As soon as they arrived at their new home, they crawled under a chest of drawers. They were scared and terribly unhappy. Only at night, when everything was quiet, did they come out of hiding to eat a little and to use the litter box.

In order to examine them we had to forcibly pull them out of their hiding place. Both had some tartar deposits on their teeth, but otherwise they seemed to be in good health. I gave each an injection of vitamins combined with a preparation to stimulate their immune system. Afterwards, the new owner spent a lot of time with both cats, stroking and cuddling them. Although they seemed to enjoy the attention, they ran to their hiding place as soon as they could. Since the problem was psychological rather than physical, I prescribed a specific Bach flower remedy. I also suggested that the owner patiently continue to try to get Mimi and Momo out of their hiding place. To entice them to eat better, the owner was to offer them chicken and other tasty treats.

The owner called me back the next day and reported on the astounding success of our strategy. Momo had come out of hiding voluntarily and ate normally after only two applications of the remedy. Strengthened by good nutrition, she proceeded to explore her new home. Mimi, too, was less fearful as a result of the Bach flower remedy. Encouraged by her sister's example, she also showed more interest in her surroundings. After two more days, both showed much less apprehension towards their new owner. Although they finished all their food, they still went to their hiding place. The shyness towards strangers remained.

General Strengthening Protocol

Many cat owners don't like to helplessly watch their housemates get older and become more and more susceptible to illness and to other problems. Of course, we need to use sound preventative measures, but with aging, the magic word is "revitalization." Enough natural preparations are available so that we can design individual therapies for each animal.

A good example is twelve-year-old Anuk and his sister Khala. A thorough examination showed that both were relatively healthy. But in spite of that good report, the owner asked me to start a

> **TIP**
>
> If you adopt old, shy cats, let them use a carton as a hiding place. Keep the carton in a quiet room away from the normal traffic in the house. Place their food dishes and litter box in the same room.

An accurate diagnosis is the prerequisite for every treatment, regardless of whether it takes place at a veterinarian's or a practitioner's office. In addition to getting all pertinent information from the owner, blood tests or other lab tests are often necessary.

revitalization therapy. First, I removed the tartar from the teeth of both cats. For Anuk, who was suffering from the onset of arthritis, I prescribed eight sessions of magnet therapy combined with an injection of different ophidian extracts and vitamins at each appointment.

Khala had gone through an episode of kidney stones. I suggested that a kidney tea would be very good for her. In addition, on a regular basis I injected her with a homeopathic remedy consisting of an herbal kidney stimulant and vitamins. We also designed a specific Bach flower remedy for both cats. On the days when the cats did not receive injections, we gave them a cell-building homeo-pathic preparation. We concluded the therapy after eight sessions.

Stress Gastritis

Older cats react much more intensely to stress than young cats do. The most common stress reaction is gastritis, an inflammation of the lining of the stomach. Typically this causes vomiting and loss of appetite.

Leukemia

Feline Leukemia Virus Disease Complex (FeLV), similar to feline AIDS (feline-T-lymphotrophic lentivirus, or FTLV), is transmitted by a particularly treacherous—but for people completely harmless—virus. The virus brings about a cancer-like illness in the cells of the body's own immune system or a general weakening of the immune system. The weakened immune system makes the organism susceptible to other infectious diseases that are then usually fatal. At least three percent of all free-roaming cats are infected with the leukemia virus (an estimation). The time it takes for the illness to become active after an animal has been infected differs widely; in some instances it may take years. Some infected cats never become sick at all—however, they are a constant threat to other cats.

The symptoms of the illness also vary widely: from a chronic gum infection to constantly reappearing colds, all the way to chronic diarrhea. Every chronic or repeatedly occurring illness may be due to the presence of leukemia. A proper diagnosis can only be made with the help of a blood test—showing the presence of antibodies to the leukemia virus. (However, there are cats that have not developed antibodies in their blood even though they have been infected.) There is no cure for this illness. All that allopathic or natural healing methods can do is to fight the symptoms and support the animal's own defense mechanism. For more on protecting against leukemia, see the immunization schedule on page 26.

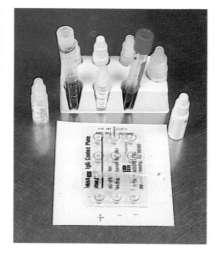

You can only diagnose a leukemia viral infection with a special lab test, and this test has to be given before immunizing the cat against the illness.

These were the symptoms that the twelve-year-old Persian cat, Pinki, suffered from when she had to stay temporarily with the owner's friends because the owner was in the hospital. For three days in a row, Pinki staged a hunger strike which included refusing to drink. When she began to vomit mucus from the stomach, her caretakers became worried and brought her to my office. The old cat endured the examination quietly. After they told me that she had shown absolutely no interest in her surroundings, I started out with an electrolyte infusion to make up for the loss of fluid and sodium in her system. I also gave her vitamins. For the nervous stomach, I gave Pinki a suppository containing homeopathic and herbal substances. I also prescribed a special Bach flower remedy, to be given as often as possible, to help the cat cope with the sudden change in her surroundings. The caretakers were to give Pinki a nutritional supplement three times a day to keep up her strength.

In order to spare the cat the stress of another trip to my office, I decided to see

77

down. Thus, you have a perfect situation for sluggish digestion and constipation.

This was the situation in Mona's case. She was a twelve-year-old cat brought to my office because she hadn't had a bowel movement in four days and had stopped eating two days earlier. Mona's diet usually consisted of boiled meat and canned and dry food, which was available to her at all times. When I examined her, I felt the constipated colon. I gave her an enema, one of the oldest and most effective methods for emptying the intestine. I repeated the treatment the next day to make sure that the intestinal tract was truly cleaned out. I also suggested that Mona's owner make the following changes in her feeding regimen: discontinue dry food altogether (only a few pieces now and then as reward for good behavior); offer only fowl and veal, which are easy to digest, and an occasional serving of fish; and finally, soak flax seeds in water and mix them into the food. That should set digestion in motion. Mona's owner could also add 1 teaspoon (5ml) of paraffin oil to every meal as an excellent means of preventing intestinal sluggishness. I explained that Mona needed to drink enough water to prevent further constipation and to keep her kidneys functioning properly. In order to help Mona increase her fluid intake, I suggested that the owner give her milk or cream diluted with water or meat broth.

If, when you pinch the skin and pull it up on the back, the fold remains standing or does not spring back into place, your cat is dehydrated. You must begin treatment immediately.

her for a follow-up examination in her temporary new home. Her condition was greatly improved. She was eating on her own, so we discontinued the nutritional supplement. She also came voluntarily to her caretaker for attention. I suggested that her caretaker continue the light diet for another week and then slowly introduce regular food.

When Pinki's owner returned from the hospital, a healthy and happy cat was waiting for her at home.

Constipation

Aging brings with it less physical activity. Cats also seem to drink less water. In addition, the metabolism also slows

A follow-up examination ten days later showed no more signs of digestive problems. She was regular again and loved the diluted cream. We totally removed dry food from her diet, no matter how much she begged for it.

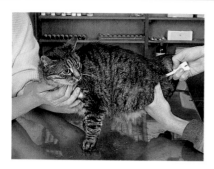

Arthritis

Joint diseases are not only painful problems for older people, they are also a problem for older cats. One of the most painful of these diseases is arthritis, a very painful degenerative joint disease often accompanied by inflammation. Once the disease has set in, we have no cure, but we have several ways of lessening the pain and slowing further deterioration of the joints.

Minka, a fourteen-year-old cat, had been suffering from arthritis in the shoulder for the last two years. When the pain got so bad that the cat could barely move, the owner brought her to my office. I gave Minka an injection of a long-lasting ophidian extract and a weak, fifteen-minute magnet treatment. Al-though she was initially hesitant, her owner finally agreed that a treatment with leeches would be worth a try. I ordered these helpful little worms, raised specifically for medicinal purposes. A week later, we removed some fur and applied two leeches to the skin. The placement of the leeches corresponded with acupuncture points. After a brief moment of irritation in the beginning, Minka paid no more attention to the leeches because the treatment was totally painless. After thirty minutes, the leeches had gorged themselves and fallen off.

The next day, the owner told me of the remarkable success of the treatment. The cat was suddenly able to put weight on her paw again and was barely limping. The pain had obviously lessened. In order to make the effects last as long as possible, we repeated the treatment five more times. We followed this with a weak ophidian extract preparation in the form of drops. The owner was to give these to the cat for the rest of her life. For the next two years Minka came to my office twice a year for a repeat of the original treatment: leeches, magnet therapy, and ophidian extract. The treatment was successful each time.

Above: Old cats often suffer from constipation. Your veterinarian or practitioner will examine your cat's stomach and belly. In most cases, an enema will regulate the intestines.

Below: The use of leeches can reduce the pain caused by arthritis. The practitioner strategically applies the leeches to acupuncture points. This is a notably effective method of treatment, especially when used in combination with other natural healing methods.

Above left: Healthy teeth are essential for a sound predator. You can prevent damage to the teeth by avoiding food containing sugar. Instead, let your cat chew on cartilage or pieces of solid meat.

Above right: You need to check your cat's ears regularly because a slight infestation is easy to treat, but untreated, ear mites can cause serious infection.

Below left: Check regularly for fleas and look for possible tumors or boils.

Below right: Diarrhea, usually the cause of crusty deposits around the rectum, can result from a serious illness. Checking the rectum regularly is important.

Checking the State of Health

When you own a cat, you have a responsibility to check the animal's health on a regular basis. You need to take your cat to the veterinarian or practitioner once a year for a routine checkup. When the cat reaches old age, it needs two checkups a year. but checkups alone are not enough. Make sure that you check on the physical and psychological state of your cat because early detection of an illness ensures the best possible result. The table on the opposite page, "Health Checklist," tells you what to look for.

Should you detect any signs of an impending problem, use the information in "The Most Frequently Occurring Illnesses" for each chapter or the information about "Behavioral Problems" on pages 46 and 47 to help you decide what to do.

Take a close look at your cat once a week on a regular basis, but don't let these "checkups" turn into stressful procedures. The quiet times you spend every day stroking and cuddling are as important for your cat's health as are proper nutrition and care. These times give you a chance casually to observe your cat's body.

Health Checklist

What You Should See	Signs of Problems or Illness	Possible Reasons	Special Tips
Eyes are clear, no discharge; thin fold in the corner of the eye not visible	Discharge from the eye; eyes gummed up or lids swollen; thin fold in the corner of the eye pulled slightly forward	Cold; stress; exhaustion; tear ducts too narrow; injury or foreign object	Provide checkup, particularly in case of young cats
Tip of nose dry or slightly moist; no discharge; no crusts; breathing is even, regular, and quiet	Discharge from the nose; gummy discharge or crust around the nose; harsh or noisy breathing, frequent sniffling	Acute or chronic cold, particularly in case of Persian cats; nose is too small or short; tumor	Provide checkup, important for young cats; acute cold, mostly in young cats; tumors, primarily in old cats
Pink, smooth gums; healthy teeth without plaque or discoloration; no sensitivity to touch; no bad breath	Pale to whitish or inflamed gums; swollen and bleeding gums; severe discoloration on teeth with brown deposits on the gum line; bad breath	Severe parasite infestation; infectious disease in the past or present; in case of adult or old cats: periodontal disease	Check teeth regularly, particularly in adult and old cats; young cats: often gum inflammation problems when permanent teeth come in; old cats: teeth discolored, teeth missing
Ear canal clean and odor free; no sensitivity at base of ear	Black deposits or crusts in the ear canal; discharge or foul odor; base of ear sensitive to touch; obvious frequent scratching; swelling	Inflammation of the ear canal, usually due to ear mites	Possible at any age; cats with access to the outdoors frequently affected
Coat shiny, clean, and smooth for short-haired; no matted fur for long-haired	Dull fur partially standing up; black or whitish deposits at the tip of the fur; bare spots, particularly at the eyelids and the tip of the ears	Parasites; infectious or organic disease; hair loss producing round bare patches, possible due to a fungus; patches of bare skin; excessive, habitual licking	Normal for very old cats to have thinning fur with bare patches at joints
Belly soft and supple; no resistance to pressure	Tight, swollen, pot belly; severe pain from even slightest touch; audible sounds from the intestines; pear-shaped, drooping belly	Parasite infestation (usually spool worms or tapeworms); inflammation or chronic illnesses of the intestines or kidneys; chronic infectious disease; flatulence	In old cats, tumors possible
Rectum clean without crusts or inflammation; closed sphincter muscle	Anus crusted over, red, and swollen; sphincter muscle open; drooping tail	Infection of the anal glands; diarrhea; parasite infestation; limping due to injuries	Problems primarily afflicting young and adult cats
Spine, particularly between the hips, well padded and can't be felt in all details	Spine clearly defined and can be felt in all details	Weight loss from severe parasite infestation or severe illness or during recuperation	Weight loss normal in very old cats
Reacts spontaneously to all external stimuli	Does not react or reacts in exaggerated fashion to your hand; listlessness; stiff posture; old cats not reacting at all; bluish pupils	Behavioral problems from abusive treatment; severe illness, usually chronic infectious disease; tumors; deafness or blindness due to old age	Reaction of old cats slows down naturally

Caring for an Ill Cat

TIP

Some of these procedures are not easy to perform on a cat. Don't hesitate to ask your veterinarian or practitioner to show you how to hold your cat or how to perform certain procedures.

Cats make wonderful companions, and they are truly loving friends, but they make very poor patients. When they are sick or injured, they resent and resist any kind of treatment, no matter how well-meaning. Often gentle force is all that will work. A cat must be a very trusting creature, be very sick, or be seriously injured to submit to treatment without putting up a fight.

This chapter will give you many tips and suggestions on how to properly and effectively care for your cat and how to perform the therapeutic measures that your veterinarian or practitioner has prescribed.

However, never forget that prevention is always better than a cure. For that reason, check your cat's health regularly. Suggestions on what to look for are listed on page 83.

Taking Temperature

No cat likes to have its temperature taken, but sometimes that is just what you need to do; and on occasion, you need to do it not once but twice a day. This is the only way to keep track of how an illness is progressing or improving. In addition, many infectious diseases have a very characteristic fever curve. Thus, a record of your cat's temperature makes a correct diagnosis much easier.

A cat's normal temperature is between 101°F (38.3°C) and 102°F (39°C). However, simply getting excited, for instance by having its temperature taken, may raise a cat's normal temperature. Temperature above 106°F (41°C) is life threatening. A slightly elevated temperature, on the other hand, is not critical. But a body temperature that is less than 100.5°F (38°C) is a sign that your cat is seriously ill.

When getting ready to take the cat's temperature, dip the tip of the thermometer in oil and then insert it ¾in (2cm) deep in the rectum. Leave it in place for about two minutes. As you can imagine, a cat does not appreciate this "degrading" procedure, including having to put up with it for two minutes! Be prepared and hold your cat securely in place.

out of the way and insert the thermometer. A cat held by the neck becomes pliable, just as when its mother carried it around by the neck as a kitten.

Holding a Cooperative Adult Cat

Let your cat curl up on your lap. If you are right-handed, turn the animal so that its head and hindquarters point to the right. Place your left hand on the cat's neck so that you can keep it in place should it decide to take off. Move the tail aside at the base and insert the thermometer.

Holding a Young Cat

Hold the cat at the neck (preferably with lots of fur and skin between your fingers), turn it on its back or to one side, and place it on your lap between your legs. With your other hand, move the tail

Above: Taking the temperature of a young cat is usually no problem. Holding the cat by the neck causes it to become pliable.

Below: If a cat won't cooperate (which is usually the case), you will need two people. One person holds the cat on the table with both hands, and the other person inserts the thermometer.

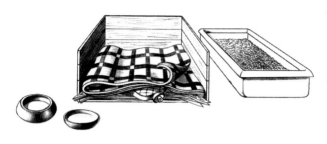

Using a hot-water bottle to keep a sick bed warm might seem a bit cumbersome because you have to change the water in the bottle to keep the temperature constant. However, many illnesses improve when treated with such additional warmth. The warmth could also be provided with a heating pad. Old newspaper is very absorbent and is easy to replace in the "sick bed."

TIP

Use a baby thermometer or a digital thermometer with a thin tip when you take your cat's temperature.

Holding an Uncooperative Adult Cat

If your cat simply won't tolerate having its temperature taken, you need another person to help you.

One person holds the cat on the table with both hands while the other person inserts the thermometer. Holding the cat takes some practice. Place one hand on the spine at the head, the other over the hips, and hold the animal down on the table. If the cat tries to bite, use the index and middle finger of the hand holding the shoulder down and push the head down also. All this sounds rather rough, and, in some ways, it is, but this way neither you nor your cat will get hurt.

The Sickbed

If your cat is so sick that it is unable to move around on its own, you should prepare a comfortable and proper "sick bed." If possible, choose one of your cat's favorite places. If such a place is high off

the ground, use furniture as steps, allowing the cat to reach the bed without having to jump.

Place a thick layer of newspaper, a comfortable blanket, or a large towel on a rubber or plastic mat in the bed. Make sure that the food dish, the water bowl, and the litter box are close by. Keep in mind that some illnesses need to be treated with additional warmth (see "Treatment with Dry, Warm Heat," pages 87 to 88).

Force-feeding and Giving Medication

Most cats cannot understand why they should have to swallow medication or liquefied food. Again, we have no choice but to use gentle force to do the job.

The best way to give a cat fluids, such as teas, broths, or medications diluted in water, is with a disposable syringe, of course, without a needle. In most cases, it is sufficient to have a 2ml syringe and a 20ml syringe on hand. Make sure that the liquids are free of lumps that your cat might choke on. With your thumb and index finger at the jaw, place one hand behind the cat's head and bend the head slightly to the side. With the other hand, place the syringe behind the canine tooth. Empty the syringe slowly, with short pauses. You can administer small amounts of liquid directly by pulling the lips away slightly. If the cat resists, wrap it in a blanket or towel and ask another person to help you.

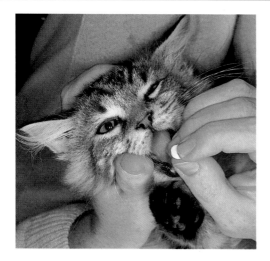

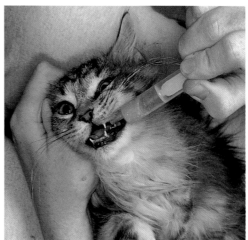

You can give very sick cats pureed baby food. Just make sure that you use ones that won't produce gas, which would make a cat even more uncomfortable.

Place a pill as far back in the throat as possible so that the cat cannot spit it out. Hold the cat's head and back, as described for liquid medications, and push the thumb and index finger of one hand between the upper and lower jaw. At the same time, holding the medication between the thumb and index finger of the other hand, place the middle finger of that hand between the front teeth and push the lower jaw down. As soon as the cat's mouth is open, let the medication fall as far back in its throat as possible. Quickly close the jaws. If the animal does not swallow immediately, you can help by gently massaging the throat. Be very careful, this method can be dangerous if the cat is stubborn. Both of you can get hurt. If this is the case with your cat, ask your veterinarian or practitioner to administer the medication.

Inhalations

Practitioners use inhalations for all respiratory and lung problems. Inhalations shorten the length of most illnesses considerably. Most cats seem to find them very comforting. However, under no circumstances should you add essential oils to inhalations. The fragrance, which even people find very intense, would be uncomfortable for your cat's nose because it is much more sensitive than yours. You'll find suitable additives listed in "Natural Remedies in your Medicine Cabinet," pages 16 and 17.

Place your cat in a loosely woven basket, close the lid, and put the basket on a rack under which you can place a bowl with steaming water. In order to intensify the steam, cover the whole basket with a blanket or large sheet.

Allow the cat to stay in the basket for at least five minutes; better yet, fifteen minutes. And don't worry if you notice an increased discharge from the cat's nose

Left: Since a cat rarely swallows medication voluntarily (unless you mix it into its food), you have to use gentle force to open its mouth. You'll need to drop the pill way back in the throat.

Right: Administer liquid food or medication slowly with a disposable syringe—of course, without the needle. Place the tip of the syringe in the space behind the canine tooth.

prepare, using so-called hot–cold gel-filled pillows available in pharmacies. For the others, you need a cotton cloth, such as a dishcloth or a handkerchief, and a woolen cloth. You can use an old woolen sock, with the toe cut off, to keep a compress in place. A compress should never be too tight. In general, animals seem to be comforted by a compress or poultice. However, if your cat fights the whole procedure or becomes restless at any point, simply remove the cloth. A compress should always feel good. Never force one on your cat.

Throat Compress

A compress around the throat usually lessens the symptoms of a cold or an inflamed throat. Place a cotton cloth, not too wet or too cold, around the cat's neck and pull a woolen sock, with the toe end cut off, over the cat's head. Leave the compress in place for ten to fifteen minutes. If you place a dry woolen sock around its neck after you remove the wet compress, you can increase the effectiveness of this treatment.

Treating respiratory problems with inhalation is just as effective for cats as it is for people. With the help of a footstool, turned upside down, and a basket that allows steam to penetrate through it, you can easily use this therapy.

or a cough immediately after the steam bath. These are signs that the inhalation has been effective, loosening the congestion in the respiratory tract and lungs.

Compresses and Poultices

In general, we differentiate between cold and hot, dry and wet compresses and poultices. Dry compresses are easy to

Compress for the Chest

If your cat suffers from bronchitis or pneumonia with only a slight fever, chest compresses can be effective. This compress is not much different from the throat compress, but you place it on the chest. Keep the compress in place with a headband.

Body Compress

If your cat is suffering from a bellyache, a warm body or tummy compress is very soothing. but make sure that you check with your veterinarian or practitioner for advice, because some illnesses worsen when you use these. In any case, a body compress is a good way to treat your cat when its body temperature is below normal. The body compress may be wet or dry. However, you should remove a warm, wet cloth after five to ten minutes because by then it has cooled down.

Healing earth can speed up the healing process for wounds that are not doing well. It is also useful in healing abscesses and skin disorders. You can purchase healing earth at health food stores. Mix the healing earth with warm water to create a thick consistency. Place the mixture between two single gauze pads, covering the affected areas. Keep the poultice in place by wrapping an old sock or a woolen cloth around it. For best results, keep the poultice in place for twenty minutes.

Cold Compresses

In the event of a sprain, a localized injury, or an inflammation, cold compresses usually bring quick relief. Place a folded, cold, wet cloth or an ice bag over the affected area. Remove the compress after a few minutes and repeat the procedure after a short time.

Treatment with Dry, Warm Heat

Warmth, the most important prerequisite for all biological processes, also promotes healing. Heat stimulates the metabolism and increases the flow of blood in the area you apply it to. You can use dry heat treatment in different ways:

Infrared Light

Compared to other light sources, the warmth created by an infrared light penetrates relatively deep into tissues, increasing circulation in the area exposed to it. Infrared-light therapy creates considerable stress on the circulatory system, so very weak animals or those with a weak circulatory system often are unable to tolerate it. Keep close watch on your cat during the treatment. The cat must be able to move away from the lamp if it wants to.

If you are treating the total cat, for instance, to raise a body temperature that has fallen below the acceptable level or if the goal is to strengthen the overall condition, set the cat on your lap. Place the lamp about 20in (50cm) away from the cat. Use the light for ten to twenty minutes. If the cat becomes restless, discontinue the treatment. You can use this whole-body treatment several times a day.

In case of arthritis or a cold, treat only the affected joint or the nose and sinuses. You can only do that if you have your cat on your lap. For these problems, the distance between the cat and the lamp should be about 12in (30cm). Place your

TIP

Potato poultices are very helpful for a congested respiratory system. Place the boiled and mashed potatoes between two cotton cloths, put the poultice on the chest, and cover it with a woolen cloth. Woolen and cotton cloths or socks used for these purposes should be free of synthetic material; use only one-hundred-percent cotton or wool.

hand next to the area you are treating. This allows you to monitor the amount of heat you are exposing the cat to. If you expose the cat's face to infrared light, gently place a finger over each of its eyes. Use the lamp for ten minutes and repeat the treatment several times during the day.

Hot Water Bottle

A simple hot-water bottle is still the easiest and safest way of providing warmth to an animal. To warm up the whole animal, replace the water in the bottle frequently. The temperature of the water should never exceed 102°F (39°C). Wrap the bottle in a towel and place it so that the cat's belly or upper body is in contact with it. If the cat continues to run away, place the cat and the bottle in a cat carrier.

If your cat is too sick to move on its own, you must turn it over every twenty minutes. Make sure that you check the animal's condition and the temperature in the bottle frequently.

If you are caring for orphaned kittens, the temperature should be a constant 95°F (35°C).

Electric Heating Pad

Because it provides constant heat, an electric heating pad is ideal for caring for orphaned kittens in need of warmth.

1. Constipation

On a regular basis, add a little paraffin oil to the food and, from time to time, feed the cat some yogurt or cottage cheese. One teaspoon (5ml) of cream every now and then also would do no harm. Add oats or linseed to the food. Food should be easy to digest. Feed the animal three times a day instead of twice. Ration dry food.

Menu I: Steam giblets and mix with soaked oats and boiled rice. Add fresh chopped parsley, grated carrots, and ½ teaspoon (2.5ml) of paraffin oil.

Menu II: Chicken mixed with cottage cheese and 1 tablespoon (15ml) of brewer's yeast. Mix 1 tablespoon (15ml) of prepared vegetable flakes and ½ teaspoon (2.5ml) of paraffin oil.

2. Kidney Problems

Feed the cat a special, ready-made food found in almost every well-stocked pet shop. If unavailable, ask your veterinarian. Make sure the food contains little, but very high-quality protein.

However, moisture and a cat's teeth and claws can easily damage an electric heating pad. To avoid electric shock, carefully protect the pad. Place it in a plastic

Diet

Fish and fowl are particularly good. Make sure the cat does not eat food containing salt. Also, do not feed dry food. Add plenty of liquid to the diet and encourage the cat to increase fluid intake by offering broth or diluted milk instead of water. (Milk, however, can cause diarrhea. If that is the case, discontinue the milk.)

3. Diarrhea or Vomiting

Do not use commercial food; instead offer plenty of liquids. Feed small portions several times a day including easily digestible meat, such as boiled chicken or fish. Mix the meat or fish with boiled rice or cooked oatmeal (both available as "instant" foods). Fat-free cottage cheese is effective because it stops constipation and cats usually tolerate it well.

Menu I: Boil a fish filet in plenty of water and mix in a 2:1 ratio with cooked instant rice. Add one tablespoon (15ml) of brewer's yeast.

Menu II: Boiled chicken with instant oats and a few drops of high-quality vegetable oil and one table-

spoon (15ml) of low-fat cottage cheese.

4. Strengthening Diet

This diet should contain high-quality protein and fat and should be rich in vitamins, particularly those from the vitamin B group. Feed the cat half an egg yolk and add dextrose to the drinking water. Offer your cat three, four, or five meals a day.

Menu I: Add brewer's yeast and 3½ to 5½oz (100 to 500gm) of ground beef to oats and olive oil, mix together, and shape into a patty. Bake for 5 minutes. Sprinkle with a little chopped parsley and chives. Serve while still warm.

Menu II: Mix one scrambled egg and 3½oz (100gm) of baked chicken meat (remove skin and bones). Add one tablespoon (15ml) each of sweet or sour cream and boiled rice. Also add a small amount of garlic.

Menu III: Mix 3½oz (100gm) of fish filet, breaded or steamed, with one tablespoon (15ml) of mashed carrots. Mix with brewer's yeast and mineral flakes.

Make sure that your cat does not become picky about any one of the foods you prepare.

bag and seal the bag with adhesive tape. Wrap it in several layers of newspaper and wrap the whole package in a pillowcase or a large towel.

You can use the "High" setting until the bed is thoroughly warm. However, turn the temperature down to its lowest setting within ten minutes.

By firmly gripping the neck of an injured cat, one person can safely lift the cat and carry it. This is especially important if no one else is available to help, or if the cat has fractured one leg or paw and you cannot transport it on its side.

by grabbing the towel and the skin at the neck. If possible, try not to touch an injured limb or an open wound.

Bandaging

In most cases, applying a bandage to a cat is very difficult. However, sometimes you cannot avoid it, if, for instance, you need to cover a wound. You must tie the bandage tightly enough so that it won't come off and so that the cat cannot pull it, making it too tight.

Bandaging a Front Leg

You'll need a small tube bandage. Cut a piece that is three times as long as the front leg and tie one end with a knot. Pull the bandage over the cat's leg like a sock. Cut the tube on both sides under the shoulder. Pull one end under the chest and forward between the legs, passing one leg, up to the back, where you tie it together with the other part of the tube. Tie the remaining ends like a collar around the neck. Finally, pull the knot up and secure it with adhesive tape so that it won't put pressure on the paw. Secure the bandage by taping it loosely around the elbow. Also, check to make sure that the bandage is not cutting into the skin under the armpit. If it is too tight, cut the tube a little more. See the photos on page 92.

Bandage for Hind Leg

Here, too, you'll need a small tube bandage. Cut a piece 20 to 28in (50 to

Rescue Procedures

We've discussed how to use gentle force to hold a cat when it is necessary to perform therapeutic measures in "Forced Feeding and Medication" and in "Taking Temperature." You can use the same neck hold discussed there for transporting a cat, except that the second hand must suport the back.

Lifting a seriously injured cat usually requires two people to reduce the odds of your getting hurt or further injury to the cat. One person should slide both hands under the cat's chest and hip, while the second person holds the legs. The two people lift the cat carefully, without twisting or bending the body. If possible, place the animal on a blanket, towel, or jacket that can serve as a stretcher. If the cat might bite you, place a towel over its head, holding the cat still

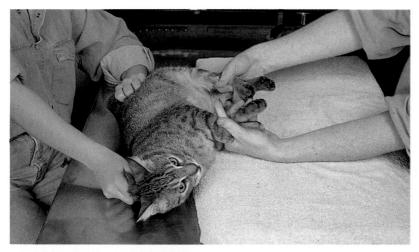

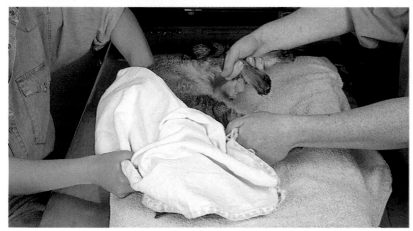

Rescuing a severely injured cat is easier with two people. If the cat's limbs are not injured, one person supports the body while the other holds the front legs with one hand and the hind legs with the other hand. The second person needs to keep one finger between the legs to avoid pressing them together. If you cover the cat's head with a towel it will suffer less stress during the rescue operation.

70cm) long and tie a knot at one end. Pull the bandage over the leg like a sock. Pull it past the knee and up to the hip, proceeding to secure it as instructed for the front leg.

Body Bandage

To bandage the body of an adult cat, you need a large tubular bandage. For youn-ger cats, use a slightly smaller bandage. Cut a piece of bandage twice the length of the cat's body. Cut the bandage in four places for the four legs, each about ¾in (2cm) long. Pull the bandage over the cat's head and pull the legs through the holes, one at a time. Pull the bandage up and over the shoulder blades and tie it together.

Finally, check the leg openings and make them larger if they are too tight.

Above left: For a leg bandage, first pull a tube bandage over the leg. Cut the excess bandage so that you have two strips.

Above right: To bandage a front leg, move one strip of the bandage between the legs, under the chest, to the other side and then tie it together with the other end at the neck. For added security, tie the strips to the collar.

Below right: When bandaging a hind leg, tie the strips together over the hips and then move to the neck and tie them to the collar.

Below left: Bandaging the body is often necessary after surgery. Pull a tube bandage with four slits over the cat's head and body. Tie the front end of the bandage together behind the head to keep the bandage firmly in place.

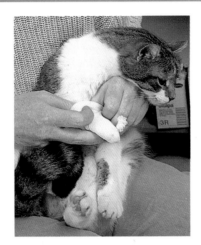

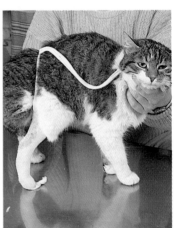

Bandaging the Tail

To bandage the tail, you need a small tube bandage. Cut a piece that is about twice as long as the tail and tie a knot at one end. Pull the bandage over the tail like a sock and cut the bandage lengthwise on the right and left sides at the base of the tail. Tie the ends in a knot and move them along the back to the neck, fastening them around the neck like a collar.

First Aid

What follows is a discussion of some of the accidents and injuries that are common to cats, as well as tips on how to recognize them and suggestions on how to provide first aid for a seriously injured animal.

Remember that after you safely rescue a cat and give it first aid, you must take the animal to a veterinarian or a clinic as quickly as possible.

What You Should Always Do

Call the veterinarian's office to make sure that a qualified staff person will actually be there when you arrive. If surgery is necessary, the veterinarian can make the necessary preparations.

If possible, transport the injured cat in a cat carrier that you open by folding the top half back. Keep the carrier closed during the transport. You can also transport an injured cat in a strong cardboard box. The cardboard box should be fairly narrow so that the cat won't injure itself further by twisting and turning inside. If necessary, make the space inside the box smaller with blankets or pillows.

If the cat is unconscious, it must be lying on its side. Ideally, the head should be pointing sideways and down. Gently pull the tongue towards the front teeth to avoid suffocation.

Administer Bach Flower Rescue Remedy to any injured cat.

The Most Frequent Accidents

Falling from a window or balcony:
Falling out of a first-floor window can be just as dangerous as falling out of a tenth-floor window. Because the distance is so short, cats do not always have time to turn themselves into proper position, and they may land on their sides or back. When falling from a height that is equal to a third floor, cats often sustain jaw fractures because their front legs can't break the fall in time.

What to do:
Even if you think that the cat is unhurt, bring it to the veterinarian. It might have sustained internal injuries, causing bleeding. This is difficult for a lay person to detect. Cover the floor of the cat carrier or cardboard box with a white cloth so that if the cat should release stool or vomit, internal bleeding will be easy to detect.

Getting caught in a tilting window:
Windows that open by tilting have been the undoing of many a cat. If the cat slips in its attempt to climb through, almost inevitably the chest, belly, or neck gets caught in the crack. The cat panics as it unsuccessfully tries to free itself, and the ensuing wriggling causes it to move even deeper in the crack.

TIP

Allow your cat safe access to fresh air, but secure windows and balconies with screens.

TIP

If you live with a cat, you should always cover the burners on top of the stove top. In a pinch, you can turn a pot upside down and put it over the burners.

What to do:

Grab the cat from above at the neck and the back at the base of the tail, pulling it up and out of the crack. Be careful!

If the cat is still conscious, it will scratch and bite in sheer panic. If you can't dislodge it, try to slide a towel or piece of clothing under it to prevent it from sliding even farther into the crack. You may need to call emergency services for additional help.

Even if the cat doesn't appear to be injured, let a veterinarian examine it.

Burn and scalding injuries:

Cats often jump on hot stove elements or try to catch the air bubbles in a pot of boiling liquid. In most cases, very painful blisters quickly appear on the pads. These are very painful and burst open almost immediately. Small burn wounds to the skin are usually difficult to detect.

What to do:

Immediately hold the injured paw under cold running water. The longer you keep the paw in water and the colder the temperature of the water, the more effective the treatment is. If the cat has injured its body in several places, put the cat in a bowl or sink filled with ice water. Under no circumstance should you apply butter, oil, or flour to a burn wound. In addition, do not open blisters that have not burst yet. During the transport, try to keep the cat from licking the burned areas. Licking increases the chances of infection.

External injuries:

Usually external injuries only happen to outdoor cats. They may come home with their fur all matted, covered with oil or paint, and smelling terrible. In an attempt to clean themselves, they probably have already ingested a great deal of the material. The result of a poisonous cleaning solution or mineral oil that has penetrated to the skin is an internal poisoning via the stomach and intestinal tract. Even the smallest dose can cause severe health problems and even lead to death. Poisonous cleaning solutions severely weaken a cat's general condition. Often the cat also experiences muscle cramps or loss of consciousness.

What to do:

Even if you are only suspicious that your cat has come in contact with a poisonous cleaning solution, give it a thorough bath even before you take it to the veterinarian. Use a neutral soap, such as dish-washing liquid, to clean the fur. Use a neck collar to prevent the cat from licking its fur.

Type of Injuries

Bone fractures and torn ligaments:

You can easily detect a fractured leg because of the dislocated bone and because the cat is unable to put weight on the limb.

Fractures in the torso are harder to detect. A cat usually refuses to get up or seems to be "walking on eggs." When a cat injures a ligament, the affected limb becomes unstable. Because of this and because such injuries are very painful, the cat is unable to put weight on the limb.

What to do:

Lift a cat with such injuries by the back of the neck, using the second hand to support the stomach, back, or chest. (See page 90.) However, avoid touching the affected limb. Place the cat in a carrier. In case of a fracture in the torso, pull the cat onto a blanket by the back of its neck. If you have another person to help you, lift the cat on the blanket and carry the blanket as if it were a stretcher.

Large, bleeding wounds:

Most indoor cats don't suffer from large, bleeding wounds. Unfortunately, the same is not true for outdoor cats. The most frequent causes are broken glass, protruding nails, and dog bites. Usually, the skin is ruptured, and the wound is wide open. If the cat is in shock, bleeding from the wound might be minimal. If only a small hole is visible, as in the case of bites and gunshot wounds, deep internal injuries might be present.

What to do:

Since it is very difficult to bandage

a cat, do so only if the wound is really bleeding very heavily. You'll find a description of how to do this on pages 90 to 92. Apply a gauze pad or other covering directly to the open wound.

Several injuries:

If the cat has sustained injuries all over its body, it has most likely been in an accident or has fallen to the ground from a great height. Quick first aid is often impossible because the animal is hiding or is running away in wild panic.

What to do:

If you find a severely injured cat, hold it by the neck and the back at the base of the tail. Pull the cat onto a blanket that you can use like a stretcher. Avoid applying any pressure to the cat's chest or stomach.

Broken tail:

The usual reason for this injury is that the tail got caught in a door that closed suddenly. But even just stepping on the tail can cause a fracture or dislocate a vertebrae. You can usually see a kink in the tail. Sometimes a tail hangs down from the injured point. Under no circumstances should you try to pull on the tail or try to straighten out the kink.

What to do:

In case of an open wound, keep the cat from licking it. Have the cat examined, because an infection that travels up the spine can lead to very severe general illnesses.

Index

Natural Healing
for
Cats